To Dad
From Ann   Christmas 1966.

THE WAYSIDE
AND WOODLAND
SERIES 𝔞 𝔞

# WAYSIDE AND WOODLAND
## TREES

Cruaidh mar am fraoch,
Buan mar an giuthas —
*Hard as the heather*
*Lasting as the pine*
GAELIC PROVERB


'I will plant in the wilderness the cedar ... I will set
in the desert the fir tree ...'
ISAIAH: 41, 19


'What we want is the meaning, the character, the
expression of a tree, as a kind and as an individual.'
OLIVER WENDELL HOLMES

Pl. 1

**Native Scots Pines in Glenmoriston Forest,
Inverness-shire** (p. 239)

# *Wayside and Woodland*
# TREES
## A guide to the trees of Britain and Ireland

## HERBERT L. EDLIN

B.Sc., Dip. For., S.F.S., Forestry Commission

*With 24 Plates in Colour, 155 Plates in
Black and White, 49 Text Figures and
Pictorial Keys of Leaves and Buds to
aid Identification of 138 Trees
in 59 Genera*

## FREDERICK WARNE & CO LTD
### LONDON AND NEW YORK

*Printed in Great Britain*

# CONTENTS

*The colour and black and white half-tone illustrations
appear in one section in the centre of the book.*

The endpaper illustrations show:
    *Front left:* Specimen tree of deodar (p. 238).
    *Front right:* Streamside alders (p. 160).
    *Rear left:* Clump of Scots pine (p. 239).
    *Rear right:* Limes in a park (p. 56).

# PREFACE

SINCE Edward Step first produced this book in 1904, there have been many encouraging developments for the tree-lover. A national Forestry Commission has been set up to promote the planting of woods for timber throughout Great Britain, and there are similar bodies in Ireland and the Isle of Man. The Nature Conservancy has been established to preserve and study, among its other activities, those few natural woods that remain. National Trusts and similar bodies have acquired many fine collections of specimen trees around mansion houses, and have made them more freely open to the public. All along, the interest of the private owner of trees and woodlands has continued unabated, while the long-established botanical collections, notably at Kew, Edinburgh and Dublin, have been maintained and extended.

Yet Step's approach to this vast field of study remains a sound one, and in revising his work I have found little need to alter it. He looked at the trees through the eyes of a rambler, following the waysides to the woods, and this is, for most of us, the first introduction to trees. You do not have to own your own trees to enjoy them; you may see and appreciate them wherever you go. To do so, you must of course be able to name the different kinds, and this knowledge can be gained by observation and fairly easy study of obvious features—bark, twig, leaf, flower and fruit. It is not necessary to use a microscope, or even a lens, nor to study any difficult theory of classification. Provided enough good pictures are available anyone can quickly become familiar with all our common trees.

Step's choice of trees has also stood the test of time. He included all the native kinds and the more obvious and common introductions; and in this edition the list and arrangement remain substantially the same. A few rarities have been omitted, and several new kinds that have come to be planted on a large scale have been brought in. There are now fifty-nine genera comprising 138 species, as compared with forty-six genera and 117 species in the previous edition. It would be easy to extend this list, by adding many attractive but uncommon ornamental trees, and many shrubs or bushes. But to do so would make it impossible to describe and illustrate all of them fully, and it is better to know fifty-nine groups of trees really well than to feel unsure about some greater number.

Now that so many tree-lovers continue their studies during trips abroad, I have thought it advisable to add the names of the major trees in the languages of other countries where they are common, notably in France, Germany, Holland, Denmark, Sweden and Norway. This book can be used with confidence anywhere in Europe north and west of the Alps; farther south and east most of the trees described will still be encountered, but the number and variety of kinds increases, so not all are covered. In North America, and indeed in the temperate regions of Asia, the same *genera* will be found, along with others not described, but most *species* differ. To aid the American reader, the American names for groups of trees have been included, wherever they differ from those customary in England.

Edward Step featured many unusual local and craft uses for trees and their timbers, and I have retained this feature where possible, but have added the more modern and commercial uses. He also recorded many local names for trees, and I have kept this feature too. He drew extensively on the classic work *Sylva*, by John Evelyn, so it is fitting that this new edition should appear exactly 300 years after that first comprehensive account of British forest trees was published.

Most of the original colour plates by Dorothy Fitchew have been retained in this edition and so have many line drawings by Mabel E. Step, and photographs by Henry Irving. The publishers have also sought the help of modern tree photographers and our thanks are due to all the people named below.

# ACKNOWLEDGMENTS

THE colour pictures were painted by Dorothy Fitchew, except for the frontispiece, which is a photograph by Graham P. Edlin. The endpaper photos were taken by Eric J. Hosking, except for the deodar which is by Maurice Nimmo.

The line illustrations in the text and the keys were drawn by Mabel E. Step and A. F. Stuart. Figures 1 to 6 are based on sketches by H. L. Edlin.

Thanks are due to the following photographers for the subjects shown:

Henry Irving for plates 3, 5, 7, 9, 12, 13, 15, 16, 22, 27, 28, 30, 34, 42, 45, 46, 47, 49, 50, 51, 52, 53, 54, 56, 57, 58, 65, 68, 69, 74, 77, 79, 80, 85, 90, 91, 93, 97, 98, 99, 104, 111, 113, 117, 124, 128, 129, 130, 132, 144, 147 and 151.

Maurice Nimmo for plates 6, 8, 23, 24, 25, 33, 36, 37, 38, 39, 40, 48, 60, 62, 70, 73, 75, 76, 78, 81, 83, 84, 86, 88, 102, 106, 107, 115, 120, 121, 123, 126, 127, 131, 133, 134, 135, 137, 138, 140, 142, 145, 146, 148, 149, 150, 152, 155, 156, 157, 159, 161, 162, 163, 164, 166, 167, 169, 172, 173, 174 and 175.

Eric J. Hosking for plates 2, 10, 19, 20, 63, 64, 82, 89, 95, 96, 100, 105, 116, 118, 119, 139, 158, 168 and 171.

John Markham for plates 143 and 160; Harold Bastin for plates 29, 31, 41, 55, 67, 87, 112, 125, 136 and 141; J. E. Downward for plates 26 and 108; Leonard and Marjorie Gayton for plate 122; J. D. U. Ward for plate 101; Graham P. Edlin for plate 110; and the Forestry Commission for plate 94.

Alan F. Mitchell of the Forestry Commission kindly provided up-to-date information on the tallest and stoutest trees of each kind growing in Britain today. K. G. Stott of the

Long Ashton Research Station, Bristol University, supplied willow specimens.

Finally, I am deeply grateful to my wife, Betty Margaret, for carrying out all the exacting secretarial work needed for this new edition.

Herbert Leeson Edlin

# TREE, TIMBER AND FOREST

We draw the word 'tree' from an old Scandinavian tongue, and originally it meant, as *tre* still does in Norway, both the tree itself and the wood of its trunk. As we use the word today, it defines a plant of a particular habit of growth, quite easily known. A tree is a land plant that can form a single, upright, firm woody stem, which lasts for many years.

Woody plants are distinguished from other non-woody plants by the presence in their stems of a central column of conductive and structural tissue, briefly their *wood*, which supports their foliage and carries water upwards. Amongst the woody plants, the trees stand out because a single, upright stem can usually be seen, though it carries side branches. The other groups of woody plants are the shrubs or bushes with many stems not easily divisible into a main one and its branches, and the woody climbers or creepers with stems that lack firmness.

## THE WOODY STEM

To understand what wood is and does in the living tree, we must look briefly at the way all green plants are nourished. They draw their water and certain mineral salts from the soil, through their roots; and they get their carbon compounds from the air by fixing carbon dioxide, with the aid of sunlight, in their leaves. The root-sap must be fed upwards into the leaves, and at the same time the leaf-sap must be fed downwards into the roots, so that each part can supply the other with what it needs.

In non-woody plants, and in the leaves and softer tissues of the woody ones, this two-way traffic is carried out through veins, each vein holding two groups of cells—one (the xylem) sending root-sap up and the other (the phloem) sending the leaf-sap down. A seedling tree, and every twig on every tree,

I

starts life with the aid of such veins (Fig. 1, A). But as it begins the next phase of its growth, usually in its second year, it groups all the upward-working conductive cells in the centre of the stem, so starting to make wood. The downward-working conductive cells are grouped outside this central column of wood, forming a thin layer of tissue called *bast* (Fig. 1, B). Outside this again comes a layer of protective cells which make up the *bark*.

As the tree grows in size it needs more wood and bast to carry growing volumes of sap. This is produced by a marvellous, but very thin, layer of cells called the *cambium*. The cambium lies between the wood and the bast, forming a sheath right round the stem from ground level almost to the topmost shoots. In spring and summer it gives rise to fresh cells on its *outer*

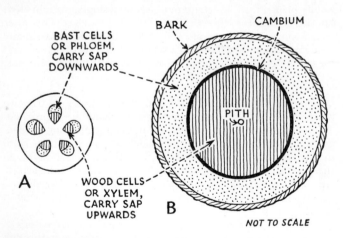

**Fig. 1.** In a young woody stem, or the stem of a non-woody plant, conductive tissues are grouped in veins, as at A. In an older woody stem, upward-conducting cells form the central *wood*, downward-conducting cells form the outer *bast*, as at B.

side, forming fresh bast tissue between wood and bark; the bast, however, never gets very thick. At the same time the cambium produces, on its *inner* side, many fresh wood cells, which make the stem become stouter. All the true wood is laid down in this way, as circular columns of tissue produced on the outside of the stem quite close to the surface (Fig. 2).

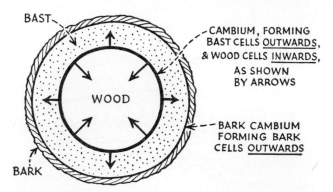

**Fig. 2.** Diagrammatic cross-section of a woody stem, showing formation of wood, bast and bark (not drawn to scale).

In the spring, when much sap is needed by the expanding leaves, the cambium forms open cells that are mainly conductive tissue, the *springwood*. In the summer it forms closer cells with stouter walls, whose main purpose is support; this is the *summerwood* (Fig. 3). Each double band of tissues forms one *annual ring*, and this can be clearly seen when the stem is cut across. Each ring means a year of growth at that particular point on the stem, so if a tree is cut across at ground level its total age can be discovered by counting the rings. No wood is formed in autumn or winter, though *evergreen* trees continue to build up their stores of nourishment during that time.

The fine structure of wood cells, as seen through a microscope, varies from tree to tree. The naked eye can only pick out the annual rings and, in certain trees only, two features called *pores* and *rays* which help one to identify some timbers. The pores, found only in broadleaved trees, are large conductive vessels that always follow the curves of the rings. The rays are bands of conductive and storage tissue that always run *across* the rings.

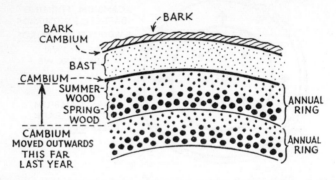

**Fig. 3.** Two annual rings of an oak, seen in cross-section. In spring the cambium produces open-textured springwood with large pores. In summer it forms close-textured summerwood with small pores. In doing so it moves outwards. The two zones together make one annual ring.

All wood serves to carry sap and therefore it all starts life as *sapwood*. As the years go by the tree ceases to need the inner core of material for sap transport so it changes this by slow degrees into *heartwood* (Fig. 4). Certain chemical substances, mainly tannins in broadleaved trees and resins in conifers, are deposited in it, making it somewhat harder, and its conductive channels become blocked. In many trees, but not in all, it becomes darker in colour, and this helps one to identify their timbers. In some trees, but again not in all, the heartwood becomes much more resistant to decay than the sapwood. This is true when the wood concerned is taken from a healthy, felled tree; but the reverse situation can arise when a *living* tree is attacked by fungi. Occasionally you will find a hollow oak still flourishing; this shows that heartwood is not always durable, nor essential to keep a tree alive, though it helps to support it; but sapwood must be present, and so must bast.

As the tree trunk expands it is bound to bury the bases of its side branches, and if any large stem is cut into, these are exposed here and there as patches of harder and darker tissue known as *knots*. Right at the heart of every tree, a thin column of *pith* persists; this is all that remains of the original soft green stem.

The purpose of a tree trunk is to carry sap which is mainly

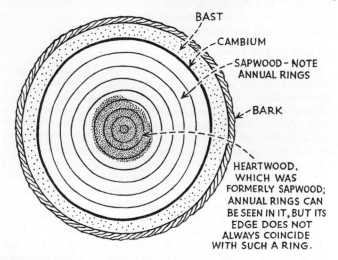

**Fig. 4.** Diagrammatic cross-section of a nine-year-old tree trunk. Heartwood formation has started at the centre and now affects five annual rings. It will extend as the stem gets thicker.

water, and so long as the tree is alive the weight of water is commonly greater than that of the true wood substance. Even in winter the sap *never* 'goes down'; it ceases to flow, but remains in the timber. After a tree is felled for timber most of this water is gradually removed by seasoning, so that the trunk becomes much lighter, about half its original weight.

Returning to the bark, as the tree trunk grows thicker its first bark must inevitably split and expose the soft tissue below. To prevent this exposure every woody stem has a special *bark cambium* which lays down fresh bark cells each year. The pattern of bark that results is different for every tree, and is a most useful aid to identification (see Fig. 2).

One of the main functions of the bark is to keep the moisture content of the tree steady, and its corky layer acts as a water-proof seal. But the trunk must breathe too, so special pores, called lenticels, allow controlled access of air; in some trees these, too, help in identification.

THE LIFE OF THE TREE

We have looked closely at the woody trunk because its great strength, long life and continuing growth are the key to any understanding of the way that trees and forests live.

Below ground the trunk breaks up, almost at once, into a group of stout roots spreading out in all directions, becoming thinner as they go, and ending in a great number of fine root-lets and root-hairs which tap the soil for water and dissolved mineral salts. This root system has been formed in a similar way to the trunk, by the expansion of fine elements into stouter and more woody ones as the volume of sap to be carried increased. The fine root-hairs have each a fairly short life, but the stouter roots persist over long spans of years. Root systems commonly run out for many yards all round the tree, but are surprisingly shallow, often only a few feet deep. Some trees send down a tap root, but again only for a few feet. In a wood, the roots of neighbouring trees interlace and criss-cross each other. All roots must breathe oxygen, so they can only thrive where air and water move freely through the soil. They are most active in summer, but some growth continues, whilst the soil is warm enough, all through the year.

Above ground the branches spread out from the trunk in a similar way, each one the outcome of the steady growth in thickness of a slender twig. If a branch becomes overshaded by others above it, it may die and eventually fall off; the tree trunk heals the resulting wound with a layer of *callus*, or scar tissue, which slowly grows over the gap and hides it below living wood and bark. The upward and outward expansion of the tree's crown is begun by the terminal and side buds, which are formed each summer at the tip of every twig; these expand in spring and grow on and up, for anything from a few inches to a foot or two a year. In young trees, and in both young and old conifers, there is a clear *leading shoot* which prolongs the main stem upwards, by a few inches or by as much as three feet in one season, or even by six feet in certain poplars. If this leader gets damaged a side-shoot usually takes its place, but sometimes a damaged tree will fork to give two or more leaders.

The leaves, which carry out the essential work of turning the carbon dioxide of the air into sugars to nourish the tree, are most active in warm weather—late spring, summer and early autumn. In the *deciduous* trees, which include most broad-leaved ones and also the larches, they fade and fall each autumn, to be replaced by a fresh crop next spring. In the *evergreen* trees, which include holly and most conifers, they persist on the tree for several years, but eventually fade and fall, usually after becoming overshaded by younger leaves farther out on the same stem.

Trees bear flowers and set seeds like other plants. Unlike the smaller and shorter-lived plants, however, they usually wait until they are many years old, and many feet high, before flowering, and some of them flower only at intervals of two or three years. A few trees are pollinated by insects. These show the familiar pattern of sepals to protect the flower in bud, petals and nectaries to attract the visiting insect, male stamens that dust pollen on to it, and female carpels which receive the pollen brought from another flower.

Most trees, however, are pollinated by wind, and these have a simpler flower structure. As a rule the male elements, the stamens, are borne in one flower, and the female elements, the carpels, in a distinct one. Usually the same tree bears male and female flowers on the same branch at the same time, but in a few trees, especially willows and poplars, each tree is either wholly male or wholly female. The typical flower-bunch of the wind-pollinated broadleaved tree is the *catkin*, a simple cluster of male flowers consisting of stamens and bracts, or of female flowers which are simply carpels and bracts. The flowers of the coniferous trees resemble catkins.

Most trees flower in the spring, but some as early as February and others as late as September.

In contrast to the flowers, which are much alike, the fruits and seeds of trees are of many patterns and sizes, and help a great deal in identification. Some ripen within a few weeks of fertilization, most take a few months and some need nearly two years to ripen fully. Many kinds of seeds are winged to aid their spread, and winged seeds vary in size from the tiny grains of birch or poplar to big ones like those of sycamore or pine. Others are wingless but large and fleshy, like acorns and chestnuts; these are spread by animals which eat some but lose others. Some tree seeds must germinate within a few days of ripening or else perish; most lie dormant from autumn until the following spring; a few, including those of ash, hawthorn and holly, remain dormant for eighteen months after falling— that is, from one autumn to the spring-after-next.

The seedlings that arise are variable in size and form. In some trees the seed-leaves remain in the husk, almost below ground; in others they expand clear of the surface of the soil. With the broadleaved trees the number of seed leaves is always two; in the conifers it is variable.

A few trees, such as Horse chestnut, bear typical true leaves from the start; their seed leaves remain in the husk, and all their succeeding leaves have the adult pattern. But others have a fascinating 'juvenile' phase, in which the early leaf pattern is quite unlike that of an adult tree. They go through an 'evolutionary stage,' producing the leaves, or leaf arrangements, of an ancestral type. A good example is the ash, which has two seed leaves, then two simple leaves, then leaves with three leaflets apiece and finally leaves with eleven or so leaflets each.

The early growth of tree seedlings is slow and they are very apt to be overgrown by other plants or to be destroyed by animals. The young saplings, too, are easily damaged or killed by grazing animals. Only when the tree has grown up above the competing weeds and beyond the reach of deer which can bite back its top, is it reasonably safe. By then its woody trunk will have become firm and its lower bark thick, and it will stand a good chance of survival.

Once established, a growing tree is well placed in the struggle for existence against other plants. Its sturdy long-lived stem helps it to take poor seasons and bad weather in its stride for it can store nourishment in its trunk. It has a large root system which again is long-lived. The strength of its trunk and roots enables it to withstand strong winds, and its height ensures that it will not be overtopped by any lesser plant. In spring it opens its leaves early, well exposed to the sun and high above the reach of grazing livestock. It has no need to flower every year in order to reproduce its kind, and when it does flower its seeds are so plentiful that it has every chance of leaving offspring, for only one acorn surviving, in a hundred years of seed-bearing, will replace an oak. Trees are therefore one of the most successful forms of plant life.

Each kind of tree has an 'ideal' form, which it can only attain if it grows in the open, away from the competition of other trees, shielded from the strongest winds and nourished by a rich soil. Most trees are affected to some degree by competition from their neighbours or damage by wind, frost, animals or insects, while many have to make do with an infertile soil. The different patterns of growth that result give each tree an individuality, for no two trees are ever alike, even if they grow side by side in the same wood, and come of the same parent stock.

There are no set limits to the size or age of a tree, but some indication of what is actually reached can be given. Our tallest known tree is a Silver fir, 186 feet tall, at Inveraray in Argyll. It is twenty feet six inches round, and its volume has been estimated as 2,000 cubic feet, hoppus measure, which implies a weight of nearly seventy tons; planted in 1766, this giant is only 198 years old. Our stoutest tree is a pollard oak at Pontfadog, North Wales (p. 171), forty-three feet round; its age is unknown, but must be a matter of several hundred years. Large oaks are often shown by actual ring counts to be over 250 years old, and I have seen a Scots pine, felled in the Queen's wood of Ballochbuie in Aberdeenshire, which was 300 years old. Many of our old yews exceed 1,000 years in age.

For comparison, in western North America the redwoods reach heights exceeding 360 feet; the wellingtonias have girths of seventy-five feet and volumes of 40,000 cubic feet—say 1,300 tons weight; while the Bristle-cone pine, *Pinus aristata*, has been found by actual ring counts to live for 4,000 years in the Arizona deserts!

Various terms are used to describe trees at different stages of growth. A *seedling* is any tree that has sprung from a seed and has never been transplanted, but the term is usually applied to small trees in their first nursery stage. In the nursery, the forester transplants his seedlings to a new bed, which makes them put out far more fine roots and so fits them for later movement to the forest or garden. So his small trees are called *transplants*. A few trees grow readily from *cuttings*, and these too may be transplanted. A *sapling* is any young tree, regardless of origin. Certain trees, if cut back, send up many side shoots, and these are called *coppice* shoots (Fig. 5). If a tree is lopped higher up, and then sends out many side shoots, it is termed a *pollard*. By contrast an untouched tree is a *maiden*. Part of a tree, called a *scion*, can be *grafted* on to the

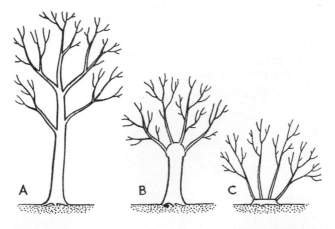

**Fig. 5.** Types of trees: A, maiden; B, pollard; C, coppice.

*stock* of an allied tree. Shoots that spring up from the underground roots of trees are called *suckers*. Finally, all those trees that spring from a common 'parent' as cuttings, suckers, *grafts* or coppice shoots, without passing through a seed stage, are said to belong to the same *clone* (Fig. 6).

After a tree has been felled it may be prepared for use in various ways. Many logs are just cut to length and used *in the round*. Our forefathers often prepared beams by *hewing* round logs to a square outline, with an axe or adze, but this is rarely done today. Instead, we bring our round logs to a square or oblong section by *sawing* them lengthwise. Some material is still *cleft* by splitting it along a diameter or radius, and so always through the very heart of the trunk, with an axe, a bill-hook or a special tool called a froe. Many small round objects, such as tool handles, are obtained by *turning* in powered lathes. Round logs are rarely turned as such (except for broom heads which will be sawn in two later) because cylinders so made always split; instead, cleft or sawn stuff is used. Fine branches, especially willow wands, are used for *weaving* baskets or hurdles; often they are cleft before use. The veneers used in plywood, in chip baskets, for making matches or for decorative surfaces, are *peeled* by rotating a large log against a fixed knife, in a power lathe.

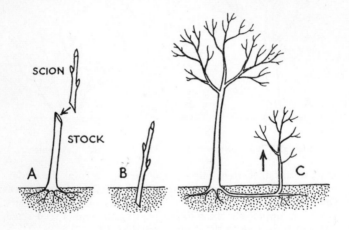

**Fig. 6.**  A, graft; B, cutting; C, sucker.

Important modern processes begin by breaking down the whole log into *chips* or coarse *fibres* so that it can be remade as *chipboard*, *fibreboard* or *hardboard*. Even greater volumes of timber are *ground* down to release the single fibres that make up *paper pulp*, and are then reconstituted as paper or cardboard. *Chemical* processes use wood pulp to make finer grades of paper, or reconstitute the pulp as rayon, cellophane, plastics or industrial chemicals.

For the first group of processes, namely, hewing, sawing,

cleaving, turning, weaving, and peeling, the users are very selective, and it is important for the grower to know which timbers meet their needs. For the second group, that is, those industrial processes that produce 'man-made' wood, paper or chemically transformed materials, the kind of tree used matters far less than the character of the process—though certain timbers are more readily dealt with than others, and so are preferred.

THE LIFE OF THE FOREST

Where conditions are suitable—that is, where there is enough warmth, rainfall and soil—trees will take the lead over all other plants, forming the community known as the forest. The main competition then will be between one tree and another for light and growing space. When a mature tree dies and falls the gap it leaves is soon colonized by seedlings springing up from its own seed or that of its neighbours; these seedlings may be of the same species or of some other sort of tree. They will struggle against each other as they grow larger, until at length only one or two survive to occupy the space that the old tree left.

On some kinds of soil, and under certain conditions of climate, some sorts of tree will thrive better than others. Often the resulting forest will be a mixed one, with perhaps one or two sorts of tree taking the lead. Occasionally circumstances may so favour one particular sort of tree that a *pure forest* results.

Most of Britain was once clothed in natural forests, but their composition—which has been worked out from pollen grains preserved in peat bogs—changed a great deal with changes in climate. After the Ice Age glaciers began to melt about 15,000 B.C. the first trees to appear were dwarf birch and juniper, bushes of the tundra. By 10,000 B.C. taller birches and Scots pine became established and spread slowly towards the north. They dominated England and Wales about 5000 B.C., and are still the main forest type of northern Scotland. The common native broadleaved trees, hazel, alder, oak, elm, and lime, reached us from the Continent about 6000 B.C. They superseded the pine and birch in the south after 5000 B.C., and they still make up the mixed broadleaved forest, dominated by oak, which is the 'natural' plant cover over most of Lowland Britain today. About 2500 B.C. beech and hornbeam appeared in the south-east, and formed forests there; but they had not spread beyond the Midlands before human settlement broke up this natural pattern of tree spread. Ireland has a like forest history, but without beech and hornbeam.

A similar picture is found in northern Europe, though with a wider range of tree species. For example, some forests there include spruce, Silver fir, larch and sycamore, which never reached Britain naturally, but were introduced in modern times.

MANKIND AND THE FOREST

From the very earliest times man has known the forest as a place in which to live and hunt; he has used wood for his tools, his house and his fire. The very word 'forest' is an ancient one. We draw it from Norman French, which links it to the French *forêt*. The Normans and the Franks, however, spelt it 'forest', and it is in fact simply a form of the German *Forst*, from old Teutonic *foraha*, meaning extensive woodland, though a Latin origin has been suggested. Before it appeared, the Anglo-Saxons used a related word, *frith*, still common in place-names and the names of woods. Allied to this are *fridh*, Gaelic for forest, and *fridd*, Welsh for the lower—formerly wooded—hill slopes. Another Saxon name, *weald*, gave us the Sussex Weald, the Wolds of Lincolnshire and Yorkshire, and of course 'woods' everywhere. In the north 'shaw' came from the Norse *skogr*, while *coed* in Welsh and *coille* in Gaelic also signify forests.

Settlers and husbandmen from the New Stone Age onwards made inroads on the forest. They cut down groups of trees, burnt the branchwood, and then, using hoes rather than ploughs, cultivated the land enriched by the wood ash. Every few years they moved on to seek a fresh patch. Meanwhile their sheep, cattle and horses grazed the clearings, so preventing young trees from springing up. Gradually the cleared land was extended, dung was used as a fertilizer instead of wood ash, and the plough replaced the hoe. Settled cultivation succeeded the old 'shifting' system, and the woods were broken up into fragments, occupying the least fertile lands. At the time of the Domesday Book, 1086 A.D., villages looked on their manorial woods as sources of firewood and of timber for fencing, building and toolmaking, but measured them in terms of the number of pigs that could be fattened on their acorns and beech nuts in the autumn. The Norman kings reserved large forests for hunting, but their successors gradually sold most of these to landowners and the work of forest destruction went on.

In Tudor times people first felt the lack of timber, and in English manors woods were fenced-in so that the young shoots springing up from the stumps of felled trees would be safe, for seven years, from grazing cattle. This *coppice* system (from the French *couper*, to cut) gave small poles needed for firewood, fencing and tool handles. Meanwhile monastic gardeners had been experimenting with raising forest trees from seed. The monks of Coupar Angus Abbey, in Perthshire, left records that show how their cellarer, William Blair, was raising ash, birch, willow and broom in nursery beds as long ago as 1460. Acts of the Scottish Parliament in 1457 and 1504 made it compulsory for all freeholders and lairds to plant trees around their steadings, but they were never enforced.

The sixteenth century, however, saw the start of an ordered system of tree planting that changed the landscape of England, the Scottish Lowlands, and parts of Ireland and Wales. In place of the vanishing native woods came the ordered plantations, ornamental woods, parks and avenues deliberately created by the great landlords. It has been customary to credit much of this development to John Evelyn, who published his classic work, *Sylva, or a Discourse of Forest Trees and the Propagation of Timber in His Majesty's Dominions* in 1664. But Evelyn himself makes it clear that it had begun well before his day for he mentions many tall plantations he had seen on various estates, and lists over eighty mansion houses with grounds already beautified by ornamental trees. One interesting early record is that of the raising of Scots pine, for which the seeds have to be extracted from cones, by Sir Duncan Campbell of Glenorchy, also known as 'Black Duncan of the Seven Castles', at Drummond Hill, Perthshire, in 1582.

The great enclosure movement of the eighteenth and early nineteenth centuries gave the landowners ample ground, free from the rights of common grazing, for forestry as well as for farming. In the hedges that enclosed their newly won fields many trees grew up, either planted or springing from self-sown seed or sucker shoots. Our 'wayside' trees are often hedgerow ones arising in this way, and most of our 'woodland' trees are the result of deliberate planting. Indeed, the Nature Conservancy, whose task it is to preserve examples of natural country, has had great difficulty in finding any woods that have not either been planted by man, or at least greatly altered by his management.

Private landowners have continued to plant, fell, replant and manage woodlands. They still own more than half the land under tree crops and take an active interest in their future. The last forty-five years, since 1919, have seen a remarkable development in the formation of national forest estates. The Industrial Revolution had made the British Isles very dependent on overseas sources of timber, and it became a matter of policy to form forests on a large scale. The Forestry Commission in Great Britain and the Forestry Divisions in Northern Ireland, the Isle of Man and the Irish Republic were set up to carry out this policy, and they have replanted old woodlands and afforested bare hillsides of little or no farming value on the grand scale. Taking the British Isles as a whole, these new forests now cover roughly half the grand total of $4\frac{1}{2}$ million acres under trees.

A feature of all artificial planting, whether it has been done by private owners or governments, has been the use of foreign trees brought in from overseas. Most of these new trees have been conifers because their softwood timber is easy to grow quickly in large quantities on poor land, and also because modern industry prefers softwood for most large-scale uses, rather than the hardwood timber yielded by broadleaved trees. Likewise, many introduced trees have been planted for ornament because of unusual features of flower, foliage or form that our native kinds lack. The character of the woods has altered, as indeed it will always continue to alter; but they remain as fascinating as they did when the first hunters ventured through them and learnt to know the properties of each kind of native tree.

It is the task of the forester to tend the tree all the way from seed to sawbench. He must be able to collect the right seed at the right time, sow it, see it through its tender nursery stages, and plant it out on well prepared and fenced land. Then he weeds it, protects it from fire, pests and diseases, and probably prunes away its lower branches. As his trees grow bigger they crowd each other out, so he removes some of the crop as *thinnings* for marketing, to give the rest more room. Eventually the crop reaches maturity, and is felled and replaced; so the forester must know all about felling and the transport of large heavy logs.

Many of the craft uses of particular timbers have died out, but the demands for wood for building, box-making and furniture-making continue unabated. Enormous new needs have appeared for chipboards, hardboards, cardboards and papers of many kinds—for wrapping goods as well as writing and printing. So the forest remains as essential to our well-being as it was to the early hunters and settlers.

Trees still give us shelter from wind, sun and rain, and we value them more and more as features of the landscape where we seek our recreation, and as subjects to study. So the need to tell them apart, and recognize their ways of growth and their uses, are as important to us as they were to our forefathers when they selected ash for their axe-helves or oak for their ships and the framework of their houses.

## HOW TO IDENTIFY TREES

Trees, like other plants, are classified by their botanical *family*, their *genus* and their *species*; each of these has a scientific name in Latin, as well as an English name.

Although this book follows a conventional arrangement of the botanical families, the reader will find that a knowledge of these families helps him little in the identification of trees, largely because the flowers, on which all such classification depends, are seldom available and, even when found, often prove exceptional in structure.

We are left then with the two other divisions, genera and species. The major one is into *genera*, indicated by the first word of each scientific name. Luckily most tree genera have well-marked characters, and usually all their members have the same English name. Thus, all the trees in the genus *Quercus* are called oaks, and have many clear features in common.

A particular *species*, such as *Quercus robur*, has peculiar characters that call for closer study. Its full botanical name, *Quercus robur* L., includes the initial letter, or abbreviated name, of the botanist who first described the species in a valid way, gave the name and published his account. In this case the 'L' stands for the famous Swedish botanist Linnaeus. Such 'authorities' for all the scientific names appear in our index, but are not shown elsewhere. The English name for this species is 'Pedunculate oak', and it belongs to the beech family, or Fagaceae.

It is best to concentrate on knowing the characters of each genus first. Once one is sure of the genus, the final step of deciding the species becomes easy. Further, most of the genera will be found right across the temperate zone of the northern hemisphere. You will find oaks in America and Japan, all easily identified as belonging to the same genus *Quercus*. Again, if you visit a collection of rare foreign trees grown in Britain or elsewhere, you can soon find your way about if you know your genera thoroughly. In other languages, most trees of the same genus share the same main name too—all the *Quercus* oaks are *Eiche* in German and *chêne* in French. Their specific name is usually an adjective, so we get *Stieleiche* and *chêne pedonculée* for our Pedunculate oak and all three names mean 'oak with stalked acorns'.

An expert can tell the genus of most common trees by a single feature only—twig, leaf, flower, fruit, seed, bark or timber. But he can only do this by long practice and familiarity. The beginner should always look for two or more features that can be considered together. In winter, for example, he can see bark as well as twigs, probably find a fruit or two that has not yet fallen, and collect faded leaves from below the tree— though he should be wary of leaves blown along from some *other* tree. In summer flowers are often available as well as fresh foliage.

Bark is always at hand. On young trees or twigs it is of little help, but as a tree matures it develops a characteristic pattern. This can hardly be described in words, but the excellent pictures of tree boles in this book will form a clear guide to the more common kinds.

VARIETIES, CULTIVARS, HYBRIDS AND PROVENANCES

Trees that belong to the same species may yet differ in smaller ways, and special terms are used to define such differences. The commonest word is 'variety', which implies a particular race found in nature. The special name of each variety is printed in italics, e.g., *Pinus nigra* variety *maritima*, the Corsican pine, a true native of Corsica. A 'cultivar' is properly a variety, hybrid or clone known only in cultivation, and probably raised artificially; its name is set in single quotation marks but not in italics, an example being *Populus* 'serotina', Black Italian poplar.

Common names for varieties (or cultivars) include: *alba*, white; *glauca*, blue; *aurea*, golden; *purpurea*, purple or copper —all these refer to exceptional colours of leaves. *Heterophylla* indicates an abnormal leaf *shape*. Variations in tree form are described by *pendula*, weeping; *nana* and *pumila*, both meaning dwarf; *repens*, creeping; and *fastigiata*, meaning a tree with many small upright branches, like a Lombardy poplar. If you visit a collection of ornamental trees you should appreciate this 'third name' for what it is worth; it identifies an unusual—and maybe attractive—race of a familiar tree. Do not be misled by form or colour; you will find all the other characters of the specimen run true to type.

A 'hybrid' tree is one known to have arisen through cross-breeding, either natural or deliberate, between two species. It is usually shown by an '×' sign, as for example *Larix* × *eurolepis*, the Hybrid larch, which has as its parents the European and the Japanese larches.

'Provenance' is a term used by foresters to define a local strain of a tree in terms of its first origin—for example, one hardy strain of European larch now grown in Scotland is probably of Italian Tyrolese provenance. Provenance affects rate of growth so it matters a great deal to the forester, but as the characters concerned are never easy to see, the beginner should not try to distinguish provenances.

The student will find the scientific or Latin names, such as *Liriodendron tulipifera*, the Tulip tree, of great help, particularly if he turns to advanced botanical textbooks or has cause to read about trees in foreign languages. But a word of caution is needed here. Although scientific names are intended to be fixed and 'final', botanists occasionally find compelling reasons to change them! Books published only a few years ago may use an unfamiliar scientific name for a well-known tree, following the correct practice of their time. On the whole, the 'common' names, in English and other European languages, change less often, and may prove a surer guide.

Botanical Latin names are sometimes highly descriptive; for example, *Liriodendron tulipifera* means 'the lily tree that bears tulips'. But often they are almost meaningless; for example, *Quercus robur* means 'the oak-like oak tree'.

The name for a *timber*, as used in commerce, sometimes differs from that given to the living tree. Two common examples are 'redwood' or 'red deal' which as used in the British timber trade means the wood of the Scots pine (*not* that of the Californian redwood tree), and 'whitewood' or 'white deal' which may be either spruce or Silver fir.

# KEYS TO THE TREES

ALL our common trees can be sorted out and correctly named, at least as far as their genus is concerned, by the aid of simple 'keys'. These are pointers to particular characters that are constant for the tree concerned. Each key offers a series of comparisons, so that eventually all doubtful choices are eliminated and the student is left with the near-certainty of a single name for his specimen.

Leaves, and their arrangement on the twigs, are an obviously useful key character. They are available all through the late spring, the summer and early autumn, and can often be found, withered but still useful, in winter. So our first key deals with foliage, and includes all the trees described, both deciduous and evergreen.

Experience has shown that another useful, constant feature for identifying the trees of northern Europe by genera is their pattern of twigs and buds. These are easily seen in winter, and even in summer it is easy to expose the pattern by stripping off a few leaves. The buds for next season are formed quite early, and it is only for a few weeks in spring that they are absent altogether. Hence our second key deals with these buds. Most of its illustrations were drawn from Schneider's *Dendrologische Winterstudien*.

When using either key, always apply it to a fairly typical shoot. Do not take a twig that is high up, such as a leading shoot, or one that is low down or suppressed, or one that is unusually vigorous, for these sometimes differ from the tree's real type. Go instead for a well-developed twig from an average part of the tree.

All keys look tedious and complicated, and some indeed are so! This one has been kept short and simple. Once you have found the answer, check it against the illustrations and the description of the tree in the main text. If it does not fit, you may have gone wrong somewhere, so try again. If your tree still does not tally with the description the chances are that you have found one of the rarer trees that are not described in this book. To include all the possible genera requires a complex, almost unworkable key, but this one will, I believe, account for ninety-nine per cent of the trees you will encounter, along waysides and in woodlands.

An example shows how the keys are used:

We will suppose that the reader has found a leafy twig of the rowan, *Sorbus aucuparia*. Turning to the key on page 24, he finds two alternative descriptions bracketed together under number 1. He must decide whether his specimen has 'Leaves divided into separate leaflets'; if not, he should choose the second alternative. In this actual specimen the leaf *is* divided into separate leaflets, and so he proceeds to bracket number 2, below. Here he finds two more alternatives. Has the leaf '3–9 leaflets, all radiating from the same point'? No, it has 'a row of leaflets on each side of the stalk'. Therefore, he must pass to number 4. The two questions here are 'Leaves opposite' or 'Leaves alternate', and refer to the placement of the leaves on the twig. The leaves are *alternate* on this twig. This takes him to number 6. Of the three choices here he must choose the third because his leaf is made up of less than nineteen leaflets and there are no spines or glands. Number 7 is indicated, and as he finds that the leaflets are 'less than 3 inches long' his tree belongs to the species *Sorbus aucuparia*, and he can now turn to the descriptions and illustrations on the page indicated.

Bold figures, e.g., **8**, are used to indicate a 'jump' in the sequence of the key descriptions. If you find that a bold number on the right-hand side of the key fits your specimen, go at once to the corresponding bold number further on, on the left-hand side of the page. This will save you a lot of time reading about trees that cannot possibly be the one you have found; for example, a *simple* leaf leads from **8** on right-hand side to **8** further on, on the left-hand side, jumping descriptions 2 to 7, which only fit *compound* leaves.

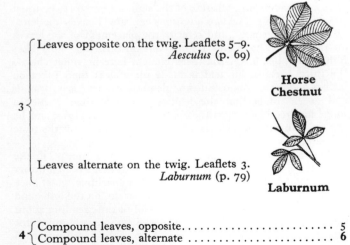

3 { Leaves opposite on the twig. Leaflets 5–9.
             *Aesculus* (p. 69)

**Horse Chestnut**

Leaves alternate on the twig. Leaflets 3.
             *Laburnum* (p. 79)

**Laburnum**

**Ash**

5 { Leaflets 9–15. Buds black. Seeds winged. *Fraxinus* (p. 128)

**Elder**

Leaflets 5–9. Buds brownish. Fleshy berries. *Sambucus* (p. 118)

**Locust**

6 { Leaflets 19 or more. Paired spines at the base of the leaf-stalk.
6a. *Robinia* (p. 81)

**Tree of Heaven**

Leaflets 13–25 with glandular teeth at the base of each leaflet. Spineless.
6b. *Ailanthus* (p. 135)

Leaflets less than 19, without glands at the base. Spineless . . . . . . . . . . . . . . . . . . . . . . . . . . . . . . . . . . . . . . . 7

7 {

Leaflets 3 inches or more in length, fragrant when crushed, entire-edged. Twigs with chambered pith. Flowers in catkins.          *Juglans* (p. 152)

**Walnut**

Leaflets less than 3 inches long with toothed edges. Pith continuous. White flowers in clusters.
          *Sorbus aucuparia* (p. 105)

**Rowan**

8 {

Simple leaves, lance-shaped, about ½ inch broad, hard and spine-tipped.
          *Araucaria* (p. 221)

**Monkey Puzzle**

Simple leaves, not as above........................ 9

9 {

Leaves less than ¼ inch broad, needle or scale-like, conifers ......................................10
Leaves more than ¼ inch broad, not needle or scale-like, broadleaved trees, etc...........................18

10 {

Leaves in clusters of 2, 3 or 5, with sheath at base of each cluster, needle-like.          *Pinus* (p. 239)

**Scots Pine**

Leaves solitary or bunched on short shoots, needle or scale-like ......................................11

11 {

Leaves needle-like, arranged in bunches on short shoots along the twig..................................12
Leaves needle or scale-like, not in bunches ..........13

Deciduous trees with flat, soft leaves.
*Larix* (p. 233)

**Larch**

12

Evergreen trees with stiff, angular, sharply pointed leaves.
*Cedrus* (p. 236)

**Cedar of Lebanon**

Leaves needle-like, in two rows, dull green above, pale green below. Fruit, a red or yellow fleshy berry.
13a. *Taxus* (p. 217)

**Yew**

13

Leaves needle-like, in two rows, mid-green both sides, grading into bud scales at base of branchlet, evergreen. Fruit a cone.       13b. *Sequoia* (p. 247)

**Californian Redwood**

As 13b, but leaves pale green, deciduous, buds above branchlets.
13c. *Taxodium* (p. 250)

**Swamp Cypress**

As 13c but buds below or beside branchlets.       13d. *Metasequoia* (p. 252)

**Dawn Cypress**

Leaves linear or scale-like. Cone-bearing trees or berry-bearing shrubs. . . . . . . . . . . . . . . . . . . . . . . . . . . . . . . . 14

Leaves scale-like, overlapping to form foliage like fern fronds, very thin, cones round, knobbly.

14a. *Chamaecyparis* (p. 257)

**Lawson Cypress**

As above, but leaves stouter, cones oblong, slender.  14b. *Thuja* (p. 254), or *Libocedrus* (p. 256), Incense Cedar.

**Western Red Cedar**

14 {

Leaves linear, more than ¼ inch long ................15

Leaves standing out in whorls of three, sharply pointed, with a whitish upper surface. Cones fleshy, berry-like. A shrub.  *Juniperus* (p. 260)

**Juniper**

15 {

Leaves in flattened ranks on side shoots, upper surface green. Cones woody.........................16

Leaves hugging the twig all round, and following its direction.....................................**48**

Leaves seen to be fixed to a small spur when detached from the twig; even in length.  16a. *Picea* (p. 230)

**Spruce**

16 {

Leaves seen to be fixed to small cushion when detached, uneven in length.  16b. *Tsuga* (p. 228)

**Western Hemlock**

Leaves without spur or cushion at base, leaving a round scar when detached ............................17

**Silver Fir**

17 {

Buds short, blunt, often resinous. Cones upright.          *Abies* (p. 223)

**Douglas Fir**

Buds longish, pointed, with papery scales. Cones hang down.
          *Pseudotsuga* (p. 225)

18 {
Broad leaves opposite on the twig, in pairs . . . . . . . . . . . 19
Broad leaves alternate on the twig, solitary . . . . . . . . . . . **24**
Broad leaves clustered on short-shoots, two-lobed . . . . . **49**

19 {
Leaves with smooth margins, not lobed or toothed. . . . . 20
Leaves with toothed or lobed margins . . . . . . . . . . . . . . **21**

**Dogwood**

Oval leaves 1 inch or more long, with conspicuous long curving veins; reddish twigs.          *Cornus* (p. 117)

20 {

Oval leaves ¾ inch or more long, with short veins; brown twigs, black berries.
          *Frangula* (p. 67)

*(contd. overleaf)*

**Alder Buckthorn**

(*contd.*)

20 { Oval leaves less than 1 inch long, upper
surface polished, evergreen. Shrub or
small tree.          *Buxus* (p. 137)

**Box**

Heart-shaped leaves, 2–3 inches long.
          *Syringa* (p. 132)

**Lilac**

21 { Leaves opposite, unlobed, margins toothed ..........22
Leaves opposite, divided into lobes.................**23**

Leaves wrinkled and hairy, margin clearly
toothed.    *Viburnum lantana* (p. 122)

**Wayfaring
Tree**

22 {

Leaves smooth, margin finely toothed.
Narrowly oval, veins normal. Twigs
squarish.          *Euonymus* (p. 63)

(*contd. opposite*)

**Spindle Tree**

*(contd.)*
Leaves smooth, margin finely toothed,
broadly oval, with strong curved side
veins. Spiny twigs.     *Rhamnus* (p. 65)

22

**Purging
Buckthorn**

Leaf smooth, margin finely toothed,
lance-shaped. Twigs round, spineless.
*Salix purpurea* (p. 199)

**Purple Osier**

Leaf with five main veins; no stipules at
base of leaf-stalk. Winged seeds.
*Acer pseudoplatanus* (p. 71)

**Sycamore**

As above, but lobes *rounded* at tips:
*Acer campestre*, Field Maple (p. 74)

23

As above but lobes sharply pointed at
tips: *Acer platanoides*, Norway Maple
(p. 76)

**Norway
Maple**

Leaf with three main veins; stipules at
base of leaf-stalk. Red berries.
*Viburnum opulus* (p. 123)

**Guelder Rose**

24 {
Evergreen trees or shrubs with alternate leathery leaves having a marked difference in colour between upper and under sides ................................25

Deciduous trees or shrubs, with alternate leaves of normal texture, and no strongly marked colour difference between the two sides............................28
}

25 {
Leaves with entire margins, or, if spiny, then leaves with a white undersurface........................26

Leaves with toothed or spiny margins. Lower surface green ........................................27
}

26 {
Leaf margins entire or spiny. Lower surface of leaf, white. Fruit, an acorn.
*Quercus ilex* (p. 175)

**Holm Oak**

Leaf margins entire. Lower surface, green. Leaf sharply pointed, stalk reddish. Berries dark purple.
*Laurus* (p. 134)

**Sweet Bay**

As above, but leaf bluntly pointed, stalk green. Fruit a black cherry.
*Prunus laurocerasus* (p. 98)

**Cherry Laurel**
}

27
{
Leaves with spiny margins, polished, dark green upper surface. Red berries.
*Ilex* (p. 60)

**Holly**

Leaves with toothed margins. Red, warty, ball-shaped fruit.
*Arbutus* (p. 126)

**Strawberry Tree**
}

28
{
Leaves lobed . . . . . . . . . . . . . . . . . . . . . . . . . . . . . . . . .29
Leaves entire or toothed . . . . . . . . . . . . . . . . . . . . . . . . . .**34**
}

29
{
Leaves pinnately lobed, with several lobes along each side of main vein; side veins spring at intervals from main vein. . . . . . . . . . . . . . . . . . . . . . . . . . . . . . . . . . . . . . .30
Leaves palmately lobed, with side lobes and veins spreading out from tip of stalk or base of leaf. . . . . . . . . . . . .3**1**
}

30
{
Buds small, not clustered. Spiny branches. White or red flowers. Red berries.          *Crataegus* (p. 114)

(*contd. overleaf*)
}

**Hawthorn**

*(contd.)*

30 { As above, but spineless, lobes more regular.     *Sorbus intermedia* (p. 110)

**Swedish Whitebeam**

Buds clustered at tips of shoots. Spineless. Green catkins. Fruit an acorn.
                    *Quercus* (p. 170)

**Oak**

31 { Leaf lobes both pointed and toothed. Flowers white, in cluster.
                    *Sorbus torminalis* (p. 107)

**Wild Service Tree**

Leaf lobes blunt or pointed. Flowers solitary or in hanging catkins.................................32

32 { Leaves with five pointed lobes. Buds enclosed in the base of the leaf-stalk. Flowers in hanging ball-like catkins.
                    *Platanus* (p. 149)

**Plane**

Leaves and buds not as above. Flowers solitary or in cylindrical catkins.................................33

**Tulip Tree**

33 ⎰ Leaves saddle-shaped, cut square at the apex. Flowers solitary, tulip-shaped. *Liriodendron* (p. 54)

Leaves rather bluntly lobed, with white or greyish felted undersurface. Flowers in hanging catkins. *Populus alba* (p. 207)

**White Poplar**

34 ⎰ Leaves more or less oval, with stipules at base of leaf-stalk. Flowers conspicuous, five petals, pink or white. Fruit fleshy . . . . . . . . . . . . . . . . . . . . . . . . . . . . . . . . . . . . . . . . . . 35
Leaves of various shapes with or without stipules. Flowers usually inconspicuous, often in cylindrical catkins. Fruit not fleshy. . . . . . . . . . . . . . . . . . . . . . . . . . **39**

Leaves three times as long as broad, entire-edged. Flowers solitary, borne with leaves. Petals shorter than the calyx. *Mespilus* (p. 112)

**Medlar**

35 ⎰ Leaf three times as long as broad, edge toothed. Flowers in clusters, before leaves. Petals longer than calyx. *Prunus amygdalus* (p. 95)

**Almond**

Leaves often as broad as long. Flowers usually in clusters. Petals longer than the calyx . . . . . . . . . . . . . . . . . . . . . . . 36

**Gean**

36 {

Leaf-stalk usually with small glands near the leaf base. Flowers with a single style. Fruit, a plum or cherry, with a stone.          *Prunus* (p. 84)

Leaf-stalk without glands. Flowers with two or more styles . . . . . . . . . . . . . . . . . . . . . . . . . . . . . . . . . . . . . . . . . . . .37

**Whitebeam**

37 {

Leaves coarsely toothed, lower surface often white. Flowers in branched clusters.          *Sorbus aria* (p. 108)

Leaves finely toothed, lower surface not white. Flowers in unbranched clusters. . . . . . . . . . . . . . . . . . . . . . . . . . . .38

**Crab Apple**

38 {

Flowers with styles united at the base. Fruit, an apple.          *Malus* (p. 102)

Flowers with styles free. Fruit, a pear.          *Pyrus* (p. 100)

**Wild Pear**

39 { Leaf margins entire or with few shallow teeth. Buds ½ inch or more long, slender, pointed. *Fagus* (p. 180)

**Beech**

Leaf margins with many teeth, or if entire, then with buds less than ½ inch long ...................40

40 { Leaves 6–10 inches long, with toothed margins. Fruit contained in a prickly husk. *Castanea* (p. 176)

**Sweet Chestnut**

Leaves usually less than 6 inches long, with toothed or entire margins. Fruit not as above.................41

41 { Leaves of various shapes (see Plate 112) often long and narrow, margins toothed or entire. Male and female flowers in erect catkins on separate trees. Buds have single scale. Seeds with silky hairs. *Salix* (p. 185)

**Crack Willow**

Leaves oval or egg-shaped or triangular, margins toothed. Flowers often in hanging catkins. Buds with two or more scales ..................................42

42 { Halves of the leaf not level at the base, leaf not heart-shaped. Seed in centre of papery wing. *Ulmus* (p. 139)

**English Elm**

Halves of the leaf level at the base, or leaf heart-shaped .43

43 {

Tree with silvery white bark. Leaves broadly egg-shaped to triangular, stalked. Twigs slender, whip-like.
*Betula* (p. 155)

**Birch**

Tree with greyish bark. Leaves oval, heart-shaped or triangular. Twigs not slender ....................44

44 {

Leaves oval with straight, conspicuous veins. Seeds with a 3-lobed wing.
*Carpinus* (p. 164)

**Hornbeam**

Leaves and seed not as above.......................45

45 {

Leaves broadly oval, broadest at or above the middle. Leaf-stalk short. Flowers in catkins................46
Leaves heart-shaped or triangular, broadest below the middle. Leaf-stalk long .........................**47**

46 {

Leaves rounded or indented at the apex. Bud stalked. Seeds in a woody cone.
*Alnus* (p. 160)

**Alder**

Leaves abruptly pointed at the apex. Nut contained in a shaggy cup.
*Corylus* (p. 167)

**Hazel**

47 {

Leaves heart-shaped, often unequal at the base. Buds show two scales only. Flowers on long stalks. Seed clusters attached to a papery bract. *Tilia* (p. 56)

**Lime**

Leaves heart-shaped, rough, deeply toothed. Fruit a berry, *Morus* (p. 148)

**Mulberry**

Leaves triangular in shape; leaf stalk flattened sideways. Flowers in hanging catkins. Seeds small, cottony. *Populus* (p. 208)

**Black Poplar**

48 {

Leaves needle-like, all round the twig, following its direction, with points sharp, clear of twig. *Cryptomeria* (p. 253)

**Japanese Cedar**

Leaves needle-like, all round the twig but close to it, short, sharp. *Sequoiadendron* (p. 249)

**Wellingtonia**

Leaves needle-like, all round the twig and pressed against it, points blunt. *Cupressus* (p. 258)

**Monterey Cypress**

4

**49** Leaves broad, split into two lobes, with
   peculiar veins, all parallel, and long
   stalks; clustered on short shoots.
   *Ginkgo biloba* (p. 263)

**Maidenhair
Tree**

## KEY II: TWIG AND BUD CHARACTERS

**1** {
Buds opposite on the twig, paired . . . . . . . . . . . . . . . . . . 2
Buds alternate, twigs not scaly . . . . . . . . . . . . . . . . . . . . . **12**
Buds or knobs alternate, twigs scaly . . . . . . . . . . . . . . . **35**

**2** {
Buds naked, without protecting scales . . . . . . . . . . . . . . 3
Buds with one or more scales . . . . . . . . . . . . . . . . . . . . . 4

**3** {

Twigs smooth, blood-red in colour.
   *Cornus*, Dogwood (p. 117)

*Terminal
bud
enlarged*

As above, but twigs green or brown, *Frangula*,
   Alder Buckthorn (p. 67).

Twigs mealy, with white down.
   *Viburnum lantana*, Wayfaring Tree (p. 122)

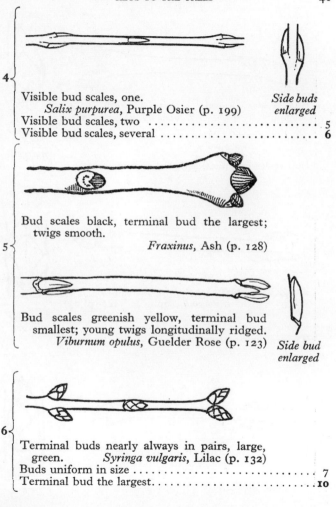

4 {

Visible bud scales, one.
   *Salix purpurea*, Purple Osier (p. 199)
Visible bud scales, two . . . . . . . . . . . . . . . . . . . . . . . . . . . . 5
Visible bud scales, several . . . . . . . . . . . . . . . . . . . . . . . . 6

*Side buds enlarged*

5 {

Bud scales black, terminal bud the largest;
   twigs smooth.
                              *Fraxinus*, Ash (p. 128)

Bud scales greenish yellow, terminal bud
   smallest; young twigs longitudinally ridged.
      *Viburnum opulus*, Guelder Rose (p. 123)

*Side bud enlarged*

6 {

Terminal buds nearly always in pairs, large,
   green.      *Syringa vulgaris*, Lilac (p. 132)
Buds uniform in size . . . . . . . . . . . . . . . . . . . . . . . . . . . . 7
Terminal bud the largest. . . . . . . . . . . . . . . . . . . . . . . . . 10

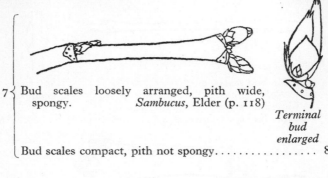

7 { Bud scales loosely arranged, pith wide, spongy. *Sambucus*, Elder (p. 118)

*Terminal bud enlarged*

Bud scales compact, pith not spongy. . . . . . . . . . . . . . . . 8

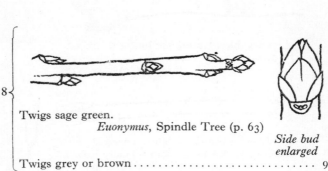

8 { Twigs sage green. *Euonymus*, Spindle Tree (p. 63)

*Side bud enlarged*

Twigs grey or brown . . . . . . . . . . . . . . . . . . . . . . . . . . . . . 9

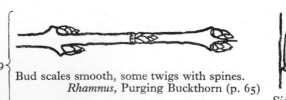

9 { Bud scales smooth, some twigs with spines. *Rhamnus*, Purging Buckthorn (p. 65)

*(contd. opposite)*

*Side bud enlarged*

(*contd.*)

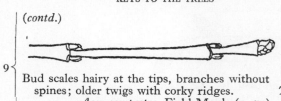

9    Bud scales hairy at the tips, branches without spines; older twigs with corky ridges.
       *Acer campestre*, Field Maple (p. 74)

*Terminal bud enlarged*

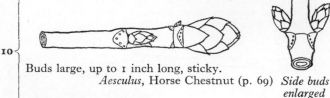

10    Buds large, up to 1 inch long, sticky.
       *Aesculus*, Horse Chestnut (p. 69)

*Side buds enlarged*

   Buds smaller, not sticky ...........................11

11    Bud scales yellowish green with dark brown markings.
       *Acer pseudoplatanus*, Sycamore (p. 71)

   Bud scales pinkish or reddish brown.
       *Acer platanoides*, Norway Maple (p. 76)

*Position of side buds*

Smooth twigs bear scaly short shoots.
> *Ginkgo*, Maidenhair Tree (p. 263)

12

Buds stalked, with purple waxy bloom, twigs reddish
brown; no scaly short shoots.    *Alnus*, Alder (p. 160)
Buds without stalks, no scaly short shoots . . . . . . . . . . . .13

13

Twigs greyish green; exposed bud scales
about four, with silvery-haired scales.
> *Laburnum*, Laburnum (p. 79)    *Side bud
enlarged*

Buds without this combination of characters . . . . . . . . . .14

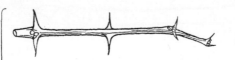

14

Bundle traces three, leaf scars with a mem-
brane, twigs with paired spines.
> *Robinia*, Locust (p. 81)    *Bundle
traces
enlarged*

Bundle traces four or more; stipule scars encircling
the twig . . . . . . . . . . . . . . . . . . . . . . . . . . . . . . . . . . . . . .15
Twigs without this combination of characters . . . . . . . .16

Buds large, conical, enclosed by a single glossy conical scale.

*Platanus*, Plane (p. 149)

*Side bud enlarged*

15 {

Buds compressed, greenish, with two valvate scales, narrow at base.

*Liriodendron*, Tulip Tree (p. 54)

*Terminal bud enlarged*

16 { Twigs very stout; leaf scars large, shield-shaped.......17
Twigs medium or slender; leaf scars semi-circular or crescent-shaped..................................18

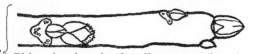

17 {

Pith chambered; bundle traces in three compound groups.

*Juglans*, Walnut (p. 152)
(*contd. overleaf*)

*Side bud enlarged*

*(contd.)*

Side bud
enlarged

17 { Pith continuous; bundle traces about nine.
      *Ailanthus*, Tree of Heaven (p. 135)

18 { Visible bud scales more than three .................19
    Visible bud scales one, two or three ...............20

19 { Buds rounded, oval, about twice as long as broad......22
    Buds pointed, often several times as long as broad.....31

Side bud
enlarged

20 { Buds appressed to the twig, exposed bud
      scale, one.     *Salix*, Willows (p. 185)

    Buds not appressed, exposed bud scales more than one..21

Side bud
enlarged

21 { Twigs reddish brown, longitudinally ridged,
      pith deeply grooved; three visible bud scales.
      *Castanea*, Sweet Chestnut (p. 176)

Side bud
enlarged

    Twigs red, zig-zag, smooth, shining; two
      visible bud scales.
              *Tilia*, Lime (p. 56)

22 { Bud scales green with narrow brown edge . . . . . . . . . . . . 23
   { Bud scales pale brown, dark brown or greyish. . . . . . . . . 24

Buds sub-globose, smooth at the tips.
   *Sorbus torminalis*, Wild Service Tree (p. 107)

23 <

Buds elongated, hairy at the tips.
   *Sorbus aria*, Whitebeam (p. 108)

*Terminal
bud
enlarged*

24 { Bud scales smooth, or hairy only at the tips and margins . 25
   { Bud scales hairy all over . . . . . . . . . . . . . . . . . . . . . . . . . 30

Buds clustered at tip of shoot, with numerous
five-ranked scales.
   *Quercus robur* and *Q. petraea*,
      Common Oaks (p. 171)

*Side bud
enlarged*

25 <

Buds as above, but invested with long narrow
stipules.
   *Quercus cerris*, Turkey Oak (p. 175)

*Side bud
without
stipules
enlarged*

Buds without this combination of characters . . . . . . . . . . 26

26 { Leaf-scar semi-circular or broadly crescent-shaped.....27
     Leaf-scar a narrow crescent .......................29

Buds pale brown, blunt twigs often clothed
   with glandular bristles.
              *Corylus*, Hazel (p. 167)

*Side bud
enlarged*

27 {

Buds blackish red, ovoid, subacute. Twigs
   hairy or smooth.
       *Ulmus procera*, etc., Field Elms (p. 139)

*Side bud
enlarged*

As above, but twigs stouter, buds bigger, more
   rounded.
              *Ulmus glabra*, Wych Elm (p. 142)
As above but twigs sturdy, buds pointed,
   chocolate-brown, shiny, leaf-scars prominent.
              *Morus*, Mulberry (p. 148)
Buds and twigs without this combination of
   characters....................................28

28 {

Some twigs spiny, buds very small, round.
              *Prunus spinosa*, Sloe (p. 85)

*(contd. opposite)*

*Side buds
enlarged*

(*contd.*)

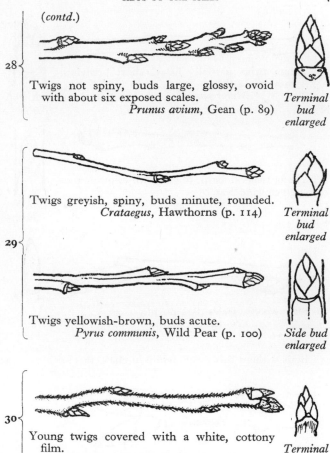

28 { Twigs not spiny, buds large, glossy, ovoid with about six exposed scales.
*Prunus avium*, Gean (p. 89)

*Terminal bud enlarged*

Twigs greyish, spiny, buds minute, rounded.
*Crataegus*, Hawthorns (p. 114)

*Terminal bud enlarged*

29 {

Twigs yellowish-brown, buds acute.
*Pyrus communis*, Wild Pear (p. 100)

*Side bud enlarged*

30 { Young twigs covered with a white, cottony film.
*Populus alba*, White Poplar (p. 207), and
*Populus canescens*, Grey Poplar (p. 206)
(*contd. overleaf*)

*Terminal bud enlarged*

*(contd.)*

Young twigs partially hairy, short branches ending in a thorn.

*Malus pumila*, Crab Apple (p. 102)          *Side bud enlarged*

**30**

Young twigs smooth, tinged with crimson and green, spineless.

*Prunus amygdalus*, Almond (p. 95)          *Side bud enlarged*

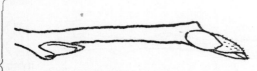

**31**

Buds woolly, scales dark purple.

*Sorbus aucuparia*, Rowan (p. 105)          *Terminal bud enlarged*

Buds without this combination of characters . . . . . . . . . . 32

**32**

Buds chestnut-brown, glossy, often resinous.

*Populus* species, Poplars (p. 201)

Buds not resinous . . . . . . . . . . . . . . . . . . . . . . . . . . . . . . . . . . . 33

33 { Exposed bud scales two or three, twigs slender, flexible, often warty.
*Betula*, Birch (p. 155)

*Terminal bud enlarged*

Exposed bud scales ten or more................34

34 { Twigs slender, buds spiky, spindle-shaped, spreading, ½ inch or more long.
*Fagus*, Beech (p. 180)

Twigs as above but buds ovoid, shorter, often bent towards twig.
*Carpinus*, Hornbeam (p. 164)

*Side bud enlarged*

35 { Twigs ridged with scales, bearing round knobs at intervals; clear bud only at tip.
*Larix*, Larches (p. 233)

(*contd. overleaf*)

*Side bud enlarged*

*(contd.)*

Twigs studded with scaly vestiges of fallen leaves; buds *above* scars of fallen annual shoots.

> *Taxodium*, Swamp Cypress (p. 250)

35

Twigs as above, but buds *below* or *beside* scars of fallen annual shoots.

> *Metasequoia*, Dawn Cypress (p. 252)

*Side buds enlarged*

# THE BROADLEAVED TREES

ONE of the two large groups of common trees is termed *broad-leaved* since most of them have leaves with broad blades, in contrast to the narrow leaves, or needles, of the conifers (see p. 214). They are also called *hardwoods*, because the wood of most, though not all, is harder than that of most coniferous softwoods.

Botanically they are all classed as *Angiosperms*, which means 'hidden seeded', because at an early stage of development their ovules—the future seeds—are completely enclosed in an ovary; this is a point that can only be seen by dissection under a lens, and when the seeds ripen they may be either hidden or exposed. All are *Dicotyledons*, which means that each seedling has two seed-leaves and that their boughs, twigs, leaves and leaf-veins branch and ramify freely. In the *Monocotyledons*, which include grasses and palm trees, only restricted branching is found, and there is only one seed-leaf.

Of more practical value for identification is the fact that, in our climate, nearly all are *deciduous*, losing their leaves at the onset of autumn and producing a fresh crop each spring.

Certain other features mark out these broadleaved trees from the conifers. Their wood includes *pores*, conductive tubes that can often be seen with the naked eye, whereas the conifers lack these. None of them bears *cones*, though the alder has cone-like fruit-bodies. None contains any resin, though a few exude gums when wounded. On the whole, their branching habits are much more open and irregular than are those of the conifers.

Among themselves the broadleaved trees show a wide range of structure. Whether we take their leaves, twigs, branch-habit, bark, flowers, fruits or seeds, or look at the finer structure of their timbers, we will find many pointers to identify each kind.

# DESCRIPTIONS OF BROADLEAVED TREES

## Tulip Tree

*Liriodendron tulipifera*        MAGNOLIACEAE

When the first settlers reached the eastern shores of North America, they found a magnificent tree unlike anything known in Europe (Plate 2). This they called the Tulip tree, because its flowers have a close likeness to tulips or water-lilies. They sent its seeds home, and it was in cultivation in England as early as 1688. Although it has never been planted for timber outside its homeland it is widely grown as an ornamental tree in the south of England and on the Continent. It is not considered hardy in the north.

**Tulip Tree**
Leaves and flower

You are only likely to find the Tulip tree in gardens or parks, and there you can easily identify it by two unusual features. Its leaves, which open in May, end in a broad notch, instead of in a point, and are usually described as 'saddle-shaped'. Its buds have a short but distinct 'stalk' at the base, and are enveloped in a *green* sheath composed of two scales (see p. 45, and note that the similar stalked buds of the alder are purple). When the flowers open in June, high in the crown of the tree, they are quite distinctive, being insect-pollinated and therefore showy, and about two inches across. Each has three green sepals and six broad petals which bend back near their edges. Their main colour is greenish-white, but they are blotched with orange at the base, as a guide to the nectaries. The stamens, with long, narrow, bright orange anthers, are very numerous and within them comes a cluster of green carpels, each being actually free from its neighbours. This is an unusual feature in the flower of a broadleaved tree; it is found in the more distantly related buttercups and water-lilies. In the scheme of evolution, it is considered a primitive state of affairs, and this explains why the Tulip tree comes first in this book, as the buttercups do in books on flowering plants.

As the seeds ripen, the carpels form a curious brown conical or egg-shaped fruit. This breaks up in late autumn to free many peculiar long winged seeds, each produced from one carpel, which leave behind a central spine. The seeds drift away on the wind. When they germinate next spring the seedlings that arise produce two narrow seed-leaves above ground, then a group of roundish juvenile leaves, and then broad leaves of the normal, notched-tip type.

The bark of the Tulip tree is brown and has a pungent smell. Smooth at first, it slowly becomes deeply ridged in a strong diagonal network. The timber is most unusual, being greenish-yellow in colour with heartwood greenish, sapwood yellowish. It is even-grained, with few distinguishing marks. Like the bark and also the roots, it has on occasion a remarkable pungent smell. Small quantities are imported from America under the trade names of 'canary wood' or 'canary whitewood', based on its colour. It is used in pattern-making because it is easily worked, yet hard and stable; also in turnery, fine joinery, piano parts and furniture making, and in America for flooring.

In America the Tulip tree, and also its timber, are nowadays called 'yellow poplar', a name arising from a chance resemblance of bark and foliage, coupled with the colour of its wood. The Latin name for this attractive tree means 'the lily tree that bears tulips', and all the European names record this resemblance, being *tulipier* in French, *Tulpenbaum* in German, *tulpenboom* in Dutch, and *tulip træ* in Danish. Our largest Tulip tree, at Killerton in Devon, is 110 feet high and twenty-two feet round; in America, these trees reach heights of 190 feet, girths of twenty-five feet, and ages of up to 600 years.

# Limes

*Tilia* species                                    TILIACEAE

Lime trees have been so widely planted in avenues and as specimens in parklands that we do not at first associate them with the wilder forests. Yet the pollen records, from easily identified grains preserved in peat bogs, prove that limes have been native here since about 6000 B.C. They are hardy trees, widespread across northern Europe; they form extensive woods, pure or mixed with other broadleaved trees, in Russia; they can be found in southern Sweden and Norway, while in Switzerland they thrive on the Alpine foothills. In England and Wales, wild lime trees are only found in a few places today, and they appear unknown in Scotland and Ireland. Their rarity is probably due to their very palatable foliage, readily eaten by sheep and cattle; most of those I have seen were in rocky places where a seedling would escape being bitten back.

Lime trees are easily known by a peculiar feature of their buds. Each bud has only *two* visible scales, one much larger than the other. They look rather like a finger curled over a thumb (p. 46). Another fairly constant feature of both buds and twigs is their reddish, dull crimson colour. The twigs are strongly zig-zagged, changing direction at each alternately placed bud.

The leaf of the lime is shaped like a conventional heart, but the two lobes are seldom quite even (p. 39). It is soft in texture and smooth to the touch and its edges are toothed. When the leaves open in April they are pale green and quite palatable, being sometimes eaten as a salad. They become dull green later, and fade to a golden shade in autumn. After falling, they quickly decay on the surface of the soil. In midsummer lime foliage is often infested with numerous tiny aphids, insects that suck the sap and exude a sticky, sweetish substance called 'honey-dew'. This stains pavements and anything else left below an affected tree, and although almost colourless at first it is soon turned black by the action of a mould fungus; bees sometimes collect it, but it gives distasteful honey.

Lime flowers, which open in June, are borne in clusters; each flower has its own stalk, and the cluster as a whole has a longer main stalk, which also carries an oblong papery bract (Plate 3). This bract persists until the seeds ripen, making recognition certain. Each flower has five green sepals which meet at their edges and do not overlap, five greenish-white petals, many stamens and a five-celled pistil. Rich in nectar, lime flowers are pollinated mainly by bees whose humming fills the crown of a big tree in midsummer. Much pollen, however, is also airborne. Lime flowers hold substances like those found in tea—the tea bush is a related plant; they are therefore gathered, especially on the Continent, dried, and used to infuse a colourless but pleasant-tasting warm drink.

The seeds of lime ripen in October as hard round nuts, usually only one from each flower (Plate 4). If you sow them next spring, few will come up; but keep them for another year, under cool moist conditions, like those of the forest floor, and many more will sprout. Their seed-leaves are quite distinctive, each being split into several lobes like the fingers of the hand.

Lime bark, smooth at first, becomes broken into shallow fissures as it ages (Plate 7). The bast tissues just below it hold fibres of surprising strength. Nowadays they are only used by gardeners to tie up bundles of plants or to hold twigs on to birch besoms, but in the past they were a major coarse textile. Lime coppices were grown specially to yield much bark from many small stems; after being peeled, the bark was soaked and then beaten with mallets to free the fibres. Recorded uses include ropes in Cornwall and on the Continent, mattresses in Scandinavia, and mats, fish nets, and coarse clothing in Russia.

The Vikings (c. 800–1200 A.D.) used lime bast rope extensively for ship's cordage. Earlier still (c. 350) the Angles had used it to fasten oak planks to inner ribs, as shown by their Nydam boat; and before that the people of Slesvig (c. 50 A.D.) had used lime planks for boat building, as their Hjortspring boat shows. All these people were concerned in early invasions and settlements of Britain.

The word 'lime' is an altered form of 'line' and 'linden', names still used for this tree in country districts. These are allied to German *Linde*, Dutch *linde*, and Danish *lind*, which are related to words meaning fibres. Our word 'line' for a rope, 'lint' for raw cotton, and 'linen' for flax fibre all show this connection. The American forestry and timber trade-name of 'basswood' implies a tree yielding bast fibres; but American gardeners and others use the name 'linden'. The French *tilleul* comes from Latin *tilia*, which meant the bast tissues as well as the tree; the first 'tex-tile' was woven from lime-bast, for *texo* means 'I weave'. The Welsh name *palalwyfen* (*palf lwyfen*) means 'broad-leaved elm'. Another Welsh name is *pisgen* or *pisgwydden*, from the bladder-like shape of the fruits. Lyndhurst in the New Forest is an example of lime trees in a place-name; in its Jutish original it meant 'clump of lime trees'.

Lime wood is remarkably even in texture and colour, being pale cream or white with no clear heartwood or other notable features. It has a smooth surface, is easily worked and is very

stable, with little change of shape as it seasons. These properties
make it the ideal wood for fine carving, and it was the main
timber used by Grinling Gibbons for his decorative work. For
similar reasons it is used for hat blocks and piano keys—
objects that must not warp or change shape—and also for
beehive frames and in pattern making. Saddlers, glovers and
cobblers use it for cutting-blocks because it does not blunt
their sharp knives. It burns well.

Two kinds of lime are native to England and Wales, though
not to Ireland or Scotland, and are also widespread in Europe.
The Small-leaved lime, *Tilia cordata*, can be found as far
north as the Lake District and Yorkshire. The Broad-leaved
lime, *T. platyphyllos*, is found mainly in the Welsh borders,
especially the lower Wye Valley, also in Yorkshire, Derbyshire
and Kent. The common cultivated race, *Tilia × vulgaris*, is a
hybrid between them, usually increased by cuttings or layers.
The distinguishing features of all three are set out below:

Large-leaved lime (*T. platyphyllos*). Bark rough. Twigs
hairy. Leaves larger, up to four inches across and rougher than
the other two; downy beneath, axils of the nerves woolly.
Fruit of more oval shape, woody and strongly ribbed when ripe.

Small-leaved lime (*T. cordata*). Usually a smaller tree than
the others. Leaves about two inches across; bluish-green,
smooth brown hairs in axils of veins. Fruit thin-shelled and
brittle, downy and very faintly ribbed. The upper leaves show
a tendency to lobing.

Common lime (*Tilia × vulgaris*). Intermediate between the
others. Leaves larger than those of *T. cordata*, smaller than
those of *T. platyphyllos;* downy in axils beneath. Twigs smooth.
Fruit woody but without ribs. This is the form which is
illustrated in this book, see Plates 3 to 7.

The Common lime is apt to send out clusters of side shoots
from the base of its trunk, which often develops burrs in
consequence. If cut back, limes coppice vigorously. They
stand lopping and trimming well, and are sometimes formed
into 'pleached' arbours and screens by skilful training. They

are rarely planted for timber as the demand is small. Instead, they form one of our best-loved trees for ornamental planting in parks, streets and large gardens. The tallest broadleaved tree in Britain is a common lime, 152 feet high in Great Limes Wood, Duncombe Park, close to Helmsley in Yorkshire. The lime with the greatest girth, thirty-eight feet, stands at Cobham Park in Kent. Ages exceeding 1,000 years are recorded for the Large-leaved lime in Germany.

# Holly

*Ilex aquifolium*                    AQUIFOLIACEAE

A remarkable feature of the holly tree (Plate 8) is its habit of producing two types of leaf. On the lower branches, where the leaves are within reach of grazing and browsing animals, every leaf has a series of sharp points along its edges (p. 33); higher up, where protection is no longer needed, each leaf has but a single point, right at the tip. These leaves are dark green above and pale green below; they persist for about two years before turning greyish-brown and falling. Their waxy surface and tough, leathery texture are linked to the holly's evergreen habit. In winter the soil is too cold for the roots to draw water from the soil. Normal leaves would continue to transpire moisture until the tree died of drought, but the modified leaves of the holly hold it safely within their green tissues. The leaves are borne alternately on stout green or purplish twigs. In days gone by fowlers used to make bird-lime by macerating and fermenting the soft bark. This sticky stuff, now illegal, held the feet of song birds to twigs.

The small white flowers of the holly open in May, in clusters in the leaf axils (Plate 9). Each has four short green sepals, four round white petals, tipped outside with purple, and nectaries. Sometimes four stamens are borne along with a four-celled pistil, but many trees bear flowers that have only male stamens or else a female pistil. This explains why some trees never bear berries, being always male, but no holly will fruit if it is kept clipped close. Pollination is done by insects, and the resulting berries, green at first, ripen to crimson by December. They then attract the birds, who eat the pulp and void the small hard black seeds, borne four to each berry. Heavy crops of holly berries are *not* related to hard winters; they are the result of a sunny summer eighteen months earlier when the flower buds were formed. In a dull wet summer few or no flower buds are laid down, so there are no berries eighteen months later.

No doubt the bright red berries, contrasting with the glossy green foliage at a dull and leafless time of the year (Plate 11), were used for decorations in pagan times. Christian missionaries linked them symbolically with the crucifixion, as expressed in the English traditional carol, *The Holly and The Ivy*:

> The holly bears a berry,
> As red as any blood,
> And Mary bore sweet Jesus Christ
> To do poor sinners good:

> The holly bears a prickle,
> As sharp as any thorn,
> And Mary bore sweet Jesus Christ
> On Christmas day in the morn:

This association gave rise to the tree's Danish name, *Kristtorn*, and one of its German names, *Christdorn*, both meaning 'Christ's thorn'; another German name, *Stechpalme*, meaning 'prickly palm', records its use in Palm Sunday festivals. Otherwise the old names persisted, *Hulsen* or *Holst* in German, *houx* in French and *hulst* in Dutch. In Wales the holly is *celynnen* whilst in Gaelic and Irish it is *cuillean*. The Romans called it not *ilex*, which is an evergreen oak, but *aquifolium* meaning 'sharp-leaved'. Holly has an Atlantic-Mediterranean distribution, from the coasts of Norway and Denmark down to Spain, thence east to the Caspian Sea; but it does not grow truly wild in Sweden or Eastern Germany. It is found throughout Ireland.

Holly seeds have to lie dormant for eighteen months before they sprout. They are best kept in moist sand. The seedlings bear two oval unarmed seed-leaves, then spiny leaves. Ornamental varieties are increased by cuttings. The wild tree is native throughout the British Isles, but is only locally common, mainly in hedgerows. It thrives best along the mild west coast. The spines protect it against grazing beasts, but in moorland areas it is easily destroyed by heather or grass fires, as its waxy foliage burns like a torch. Surviving trees can be found by streamsides or on rock faces, where fires cannot spread.

Below its smooth grey bark the holly tree holds a dense, heavy, hard, white wood which is well suited to turnery, inlaid work and wood carving. It is the best of all firewoods, burning freely as soon as cut, without any seasoning.

Holly hedges are often used in gardens, since the tree stands clipping well, but seldom around fields as the stems cannot be trained as readily as those of hawthorn. The many decorative garden kinds include trees with yellow berries, white berries, variegated leaves, smooth leaves only and 'hedgehog hollies', bearing spines on the face of the leaf as well as its edges.

Some of our biggest trees are in the New Forest, though the record for height, seventy-one feet, comes from a tree four and a half feet round, at Theydon Grove in Essex. 'Holm' is an old English name for holly and the district called Holmesdale, on the greensand between Reigate and Guildford, includes a Holmwood still rich in holly trees. This was the home country of John Evelyn who lived at Wotton; he grew a wonderful holly hedge at Sayes Court in Deptford, 400 feet long, nine feet high and five feet through, but this was wrecked by Peter the Great, Czar of Russia, when he resided there to study shipbuilding on the Thames. Another Saxon name was *holegn*, and the tree is still 'hollin' in Lancashire—hence Hollins and similar place-names.

# Spindle Tree

*Euonymus europaeus*                    CELASTRACEAE

On the chalk downs of southern England, and locally on
lime-rich soils as far north as the Scottish Lowlands, you will
find along the hedgerows this remarkable small tree or shrub
(Plate 10). It is native in Ireland and also widespread across
Europe. It can be known at once by its green twigs, bearing
green buds in opposite pairs (p. 42). Looking down each
branch you will see that most twigs become square, not round
in outline, through the development of corky ribs. Further
down still a rough, pale brown bark is formed. Below the bark
lies the remarkably firm smooth whitish wood that gives the
tree its name. Although it is so small, it really *was* used for
spindles in the days before even the old-fashioned spinning
wheel had been invented. Women twirled a stick between their
fingers to draw out wool into thread; and the spindle whorls,
round lumps of stone with a hole in the centre, found at many
ancient habitation sites, were stuck on the end of the spindle
to give it rotary momentum.

A smooth strong wood which did not splinter was needed
for spinning, and the early recognition of the Spindle tree's
suitability is shown by its names—*Spindelbaum* in German,
*Spindelboom* in Dutch, and *spindel træ* in Danish. The Danes
also call it *benved*, bonewood. Its French names are *fusain*,
from *fuseau*, a spindle, and *bois carré*, square wood, from its
twigs. *Euonymus* is 'botanists' Latin', and means a 'worthy
tree'. In Welsh it is called *llwyn addurnol*, the decorative
bush, because of the beauty of its fruits; but more usually
*piswydden*, because of their purgative or diuretic properties.
The Irish name is *feoras*.

Spindle leaves, borne in opposite pairs, are shortly stalked,
and narrowly oval. They have a toothed edge and a pointed
tip. They are a pleasing mid-green in colour, and fade in
autumn to attractive shades of purplish brown.

The flowers of the Spindle tree are small and greenish-white, so rarely attract attention. They are borne in clusters in the leaf axils and open in June. Each has four sepals, four free petals, and either four stamens or else a four-celled pistil. They are pollinated by insects. Spindle is one of the few trees that are either wholly male or wholly female, so some trees never bear berries. Each female flower produces a four-lobed seed

**Spindle Tree in fruit**
A, flowers

pod, which is green at first but changes to a vivid pink by October (Plate 14). Later it splits open to expose the seeds, each of which is covered by a bright orange pulpy coat called an 'aril'. This unusual colour contrast attracts many people, who gather Spindle boughs in autumn for indoor display. It also attracts the birds, who spread the hard white seeds. The orange aril yields a yellow dye, and the pink seed coat a red one. The fruits are said to be poisonous to people and sheep, though not to birds. According to Linnaeus, they yield a shining hair-rinse; but if powdered, will kill lice. The aril is a violent purgative.

Spindle wood yields a fine charcoal for artists' drawings. The tree can be raised readily from seed, provided it is kept in moist sand for six months before sowing. The seedling has a long slender stalk and two small oval seed-leaves.

## Purging Buckthorn

*Rhamnus cathartica*                    RHAMNACEAE

Common on chalk downs in the south and on limestones as far north as Cumberland, this peculiar small tree is scarce everywhere else in Britain. It grows throughout Ireland and over most of Europe, including Scandinavia. It is easily known as it is the only tree that has both *paired* buds and thorns. Close inspection shows three sorts of twigs: long shoots that extend growth; short shoots that bear leaves and flowers but remain short; and shoots modified into spines. The leaves are oval, pale green, with curving veins and a toothed edge, and are about two inches long, with long stalks (Plate 17). The buds are clad in bluish-brown scales (p. 42).

Though often a mere bush, the Purging buckthorn can form a tree twenty feet tall, with a trunk thirty inches round. The bark is smooth and almost black, but if a piece be detached it will show an orange surface, crossed by white fibres, within. The trunk has a pale yellow sapwood and a reddish brown heart, but is too small to merit any particular uses; it is hard and firm, with a flame-like grain.

Male and female flowers are borne in May on separate trees, in clusters on the short shoots. Though they are pollinated by insects they lack petals, and each has only four green sepals,

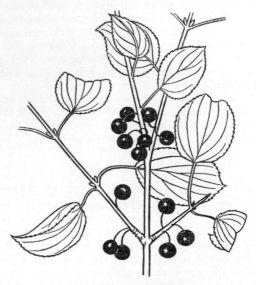

**Purging Buckthorn**
Opposite leaves with toothed edges; black berries

with either four stamens or else a four-celled pistil. Being very small, a quarter of an inch long, they are seldom noticed. The female flowers produce small berries, about the size of a wheat grain, which ripen through green to a glossy black and are very conspicuous by late autumn. Each holds four hard seeds which are spread by the birds. If humans eat these berries they act as a powerful purgative. They are still used in herbal medicine; hence the tree's name. The drug cascara is obtained from the bark of a related tree, the Californian Cascara buckthorn, *Rhamnus purshianus*.

The name 'buckthorn' arises from the strong resemblance of the short shoots, spiny or otherwise, to the short, knobbly horns of the roe deer buck. In Germany this tree is called *Kreuzdorn*, cross-thorn, and in Danish *korsved*, cross-wood, because of an old religious belief that the oppositely placed thorns were held to represent Christ's crucifixion, symbolism which can be seen at the foot of Plate 17. The word *rhamnus* is Greek for an unidentified tree. The French name is *nerprun*, the Welsh *rhafnwydden* and the Irish *ramdraigean*.

## Alder Buckthorn

*Frangula alnus*                                    RHAMNACEAE

The name 'Alder buckthorn' was invented by botanists after they had discovered this tree's relationship to the Purging buckthorn, which is far from obvious for it has no thorns at all! It grows in quite different places, never on chalk or lime-stone but often in fens or boggy woods with an acid soil. You may know it by its oval long-stalked leaves which are more or less oppositely set. They have a smooth edge and many short, nearly straight veins. Dark green in summer, they take on pleasing russet tints in autumn (Plate 18). These leaves form the food of the rare brimstone butterfly. The buds are 'naked', lacking outer scales, though they have brown hairs. There are no short shoots.

The tiny green flowers, which are insect-pollinated, open in May, in clusters in leaf axils. Each has five sepals, five stamens and a five-celled ovary. By autumn they develop into con-spicuous and beautiful berries that ripen through green, white and scarlet to black. They hold hard black seeds, which are spread by birds. When they sprout the seed-leaves remain in the seed.

Rarely more than a small tree (Plate 12), the Alder buck-thorn grows in marshy places where the true alder is common. It is often called 'berry-bearing alder', but its commonest true English name is 'black dogwood', dogwood indicating a hard wood suitable for sharp 'dogs' or wooden spikes. In Danish it is *tørst*, while its German name, *Pulverholz*, powder-

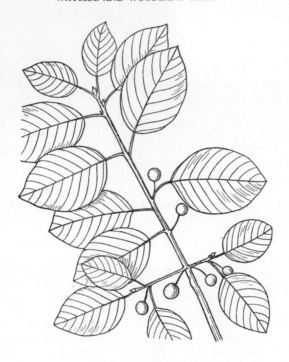

**Alder Buckthorn**
Paired leaves with smooth edges ; also berries

wood, records the main modern use of the small timber, which is yellow, with a reddish brown heartwood.

The charcoal of Alder buckthorn is the best in the world for gunpowder-making, because it is very fine and even-grained. This was well-known when gunpowder was used in small fire-arms; and realized again when slow-burning fuses were used for timed explosives in the 1939–45 war. Regions where this tree is common, such as the New Forest and the Cambridgeshire fens, were then scoured for supplies. The bark stripped from the thin stems was used to yield purgative medicines. It is black outside with prominent brown pores; if scratched it shows a brick-red underbark colour, but it is a bright lemon-yellow shade within.

The generic name *frangula*, meaning breakable, refers to its brittle twigs, while *alnus* is Latin for alder. The Welsh name, *brauwydden* or brittle-tree, conveys the same idea. In France it is called *bourdaine*. Alder buckthorn grows wild throughout England, Wales and Ireland, and the southern half of Scotland. It can be found in most countries on the European mainland.

# Horse Chestnut

*Aesculus hippocastanum*   HIPPOCASTANACEAE

The Horse chestnut is readily known by its large palmately compound leaf, which has from three to seven leaflets spreading out, like the fingers of the hand, from a long stalk. The shape of the leaf as a whole is roundish, but each leaflet gets broader towards the tip, then suddenly narrows to a point. It has marked side veins (p. 24). The leaves, like the buds which bear them, are placed in opposite pairs. The winter buds are exceptionally large, and beneath each is a horse-shoe-shaped scar carrying vein-traces which have been likened to the nails of a horse's shoe (p. 43). Each oval bud is dark brown in winter, but it becomes, especially in spring, coated in a shiny sticky resin that oozes from its surface, giving the well-known 'sticky bud'. This opens in April to reveal the unfolding leaf, shoot or flower spike nestling in a covering of pale-brown down. These buds will open indoors if placed in a vase of water, as well as on the tree, and are therefore often used for decorations.

The flowers of the Horse chestnut are a glorious sight when they open in May. They are placed well above the foliage so as to attract the bees which seek their nectar (Plates 13, 32). They are grouped in spikes with the youngest flower towards the tip, and each flower stands on its own short side stalk. The flower is not truly round, but is shaped so as to lead a bee on a set course towards its centre. It has five green sepals and four or five white petals, each marked with a yellow blotch that later turns pale crimson; the blotches serve as honey-guides to the bees. There are five to eight stamens which curve forward and downward and, in most though not all flowers, a three-celled pistil. This is hairy at first, and as it ripens the hairs become stout, sharp spines, while its outer skin develops into a tough, thick, leathery casing which is green at first but later dark brown. This spiky fruit falls intact from the tree, then splits open; within, resting on white flesh, there are one or two (rarely three) hard brown nuts, always called 'conkers'. These are glossy dark brown, with a paler oval patch on one side (Plate 21).

Boys gather these nuts to play the game of conkers, originally 'conquerors'. Each nut is threaded on a string, and two boys take it in turns to hit one another's nut until the softer one breaks. Those nuts that escape such a fate lie on the ground until spring, when they sprout readily. Their seed-leaves remain hidden within the nut; a root appears, and then a shoot which bears the typical compound leaf right from the outset. The nuts are no good to eat, and even horses refuse them, though deer and cattle like them.

Horse chestnut bark soon becomes dark brown and rough, and bears characteristic shallow squarish plates (Plate 16). Often it has a spiral pattern, indicating spiral grain in the wood below. The wood is pale brown to whitish, and smooth with no clear features. It is soft and easy to work, but not strong. Occasionally it is used for objects like trays or toys, especially for fruit storage as it is absorbent, but there is no real demand for it. The tree is grown solely for its beauty, and is therefore a park tree rather than a woodland one (Plates 13, 15). There is one 125 feet tall at Petworth in Sussex, and another one twenty-one feet round at Hatfield Forest in Essex. The branches of a typical Horse chestnut sweep down in long graceful curves, bending up again near their tips.

The Horse chestnut is a native of the Balkans and Asia Minor, and was first noted at Constantinople in 1557, by the Italian botanist Pierandrea Mattioli (or Matthiolus). He found that the Turks used the nuts as a drug to cure coughs in horses, and called it *atkastane*, or 'horse-chestnut'. It was soon cultivated in western Europe, and was planted by the botanist Tradescant at Lambeth in London about the year 1633. Most of its names are translations of the Turkish, including *Rosskastanie* in Germany and *hestekastanie* in Scandinavia. *Aesculus* is the Latin name of an unidentified tree with an edible fruit, while *hippocastanum* is a 'Greek' word for horse-chestnut invented by the Frenchman Joseph de Tournefort about 1700. The French, however, call the tree *marronier d'Inde*, chestnut tree of India, in the belief that it came from that country, though colloquially its fruit is *châtaigne*. In America it is called 'buckeye', because the pale patch on the dark nut resembles the eye of a deer. Related wild trees are found in both India and North America. The Welsh name is *pren cnau cyffylog*, the horse nut tree.

The Red horse chestnut, *Aesculus × carnea*, is a hybrid between the common kind and the American Red buckeye, *A. pavia*. It comes readily from seed, but most red-flowered trees have been grafted on the common stock and show a union.

## Sycamore

*Acer pseudoplatanus* ACERACEAE

The shapely sycamore has long been well-established in our woods where it grows freely from self-sown seed, yet it is an introduced tree which was brought to England about 500 years ago. Writers in the sixteenth century speak of it as something already well-known. About that time it was taken, independently, to Scotland, where it was given the name of

6

'plane', still generally used there for both tree and timber. Because the leaves of the two trees are much alike there is often confusion between sycamore and the true plane (p. 149); but they are easily told apart because on sycamore twigs the leaves and buds are always *opposite*, whereas on the true plane, of the genus *Platanus*, they are alternate. Sycamore, in fact, is a typical member of the maple genus, as its Latin name, *Acer*, shows. The specific name, *pseudoplatanus*, means 'false plane' and reminds us that it is *not* a true one. In America this tree is called 'European maple' or 'planetree maple' and the name 'sycamore' is given to the true plane. The original 'sycamore' was the *sycomorus* or 'fig-mulberry' of the Bible, an eastern tree with a similar lobed leaf.

Sycamore is native to central Europe, where it is considered a hardy upland tree. In the British Isles it shows exceptional resistance to strong winds, and is often planted near the sea coast or to provide shelter for upland farms. It forms the most northerly woodland in Scotland, at the Castle of Mey in Caithness, and grows better than other trees in the Orkney and Shetland Islands and the Outer Hebrides. It is widely grown in mixed broadleaved woodlands, and as a park tree, reaching a good timber size (Plates 20, 22). Our tallest sycamore, at Cobham Hall, Kent, is 117 feet high, while our stoutest, at Birnam in Perthshire, measures twenty-two feet round. The wood is very pale brown or creamy white and shows no clear heartwood. It is hard and strong and finishes well with a pleasing smooth surface and is pale brownish cream when seasoned. Since it has no natural durability it is not used out of doors. It burns well and branches make good firewood.

Sycamore timber has many special uses which ensure high prices for the best logs: it is a good furniture wood and provides smooth floors for dance halls; in the textile trades it is used for rollers, bobbins and spools; for purposes where a clean smooth wood is needed in contact with food it is ideal, serving as dressers, bowls, spoons, butter prints and so on; it is the only timber used for the back, sides and stock of violins and similar string instruments, though their belly is always of spruce; turners use it for round or half-round articles of all kinds, and artistic wood-carvers find it an attractive material.

Big sycamore trunks have a special value for cutting decorative veneers, pale in shade but with a pleasing figure. Occasionally a trunk will show an irregular pattern of grain, the well-known 'ripple' or 'fiddle-back' figure, which is attractive because the veneered surface reflects light in a wavy fashion; such a tree, if large enough for veneer, is worth up to £500. More rarely still, a cluster of buried twigs may produce the 'birds-eye' figure, with scattered groups of concentric rings like little birds' eyes. Sycamore wood is often marketed as 'maple', while if stained grey it becomes 'harewood'.

Sycamore bark is at first smooth and grey, but on old trunks it flakes off in squarish plates (Plate 23), and eventually the surface becomes rough and fawn-brown in colour. Old twigs are dark grey, but younger ones are greenish-brown. They bear buds in opposite pairs, with clear leaf-scars below them (p. 43). In winter these buds are always *green*, a feature that distinguishes them from other trees that also have opposite buds; but when they open, large conspicuous inner red bud-scales appear. The leaves, borne on long reddish stalks, are palmately lobed, having five lobes each with its main vein running out from the base. The leaf margin has rounded indentations (p. 31).

Sycamore flowers are borne in long hanging clusters, and open in May (Plate 24); they are very dainty, but attract little notice because of their greenish-yellow colour. Each group, technically a branched raceme, has from sixty to 100 flowers, with the youngest ones towards its tip. The main flower-stalk bears numerous branches, each carrying from one to four small flowers. Although stamens and an ovary are found in all the flowers, some are functionally male and others female. Male flowers, borne mostly towards the tip of the flower-shoot, have five sepals, five petals, eight large stamens and a small pistil. Female flowers are similar, but the pistil is well developed, with two distinct stigmas. All the flowers have a faint scent and bear nectar to attract bees, but some of the pollen is wind-borne.

The pistils ripen rapidly during summer to form a two-seeded fruit with a broad wing on either side; this is green at first but becomes brown by October (Plate 35). Winter winds then tear the seeds from the tree, usually separately but sometimes together, and once they become air-borne they twirl round like the blades of a helicopter; they can easily be carried for 100 yards. The seeds lie dormant on the moist earth until the warmth of spring causes them to sprout. Within each seed there are two long strap-shaped seed leaves which are, surprisingly, green from the time of ripening, onwards. The seedling unfolds these on a deep red stalk, and sends down a tap root. The first true leaves are oval and pointed, but not lobed; normal lobed leaves follow. Sycamore bears seed freely every year and the wind carries seeds to unlikely spots, such as town yards where trees spring up vigorously unless checked. Sycamore also tries to colonize gardens. The tree is easily raised in the nursery from seed stored in moist sand, and a good deal is planted commercially. A remarkable purple-leaved strain, variety *purpurea*, is sometimes grown for decoration.

The Welsh name for sycamore is *masarnen mwyaf*, meaning great maple. It is naturalized in many Welsh districts and also throughout Ireland. In France it is called *erable sycomore*, in Holland *ahorn* or *eschdoorn*, and in Germany *Bergahorn*, or mountain maple. In Denmark it is known as *ær*, in Sweden as *tysk lönn* or German maple, and in Norway as *platanløn*, or plane-maple.

# Maples

*Acer* species                                         ACERACEAE

The native Field maple grows as a wayside tree from the Firth of Forth southwards, and also throughout Ireland. It is

more common on chalk and limestone soils than elsewhere, and
it is often seen on the downs of the south-east, where it
reaches its best development. Trees up to sixty feet high and
four feet round are frequent in Surrey, but on the whole Field
maple ranks as a small tree or shrub (Plate 19) which is often
lopped to form part of a hedge. Since other maples grow larger

**Field Maple in fruit**

or are more brightly coloured, it is rarely planted, though its
foliage and seeds are both attractive.

Field maple resembles sycamore which belongs to the same
*Acer* genus; but there are several clear distinctions. The
opposite winter buds are small and brown (p. 43), and the
slender twigs have brown bark. The bark of the trunk is rough

and again brown in colour. The leaves, though five-lobed like those of sycamore, have deeper bays or gaps between the lobes, and bear rounded projections, rather than teeth, on each lobe. They are also smaller. In autumn they fade to a bright golden shade never seen on sycamore. The flowers have a similar pattern, but the seeds have much broader wings which are tinged with red and set opposite each other in a straight line, not at a sharp angle like the wings of a sycamore. They do not germinate until eighteen months after falling. Their first true leaves are simple, unlobed ones.

Before sycamore became available the white smooth wood of Field maple was prized for fine turned bowls and carved work. It is still occasionally used for wood turning or as hedge stakes. It burns well.

In Wales the Field maple is called *masarnen lleiaf*, or small maple. In France it is the *erable champêtre*, while its Latin name is *Acer campestre*, both meaning Field maple. The Germans likewise call it *Feldahorn* and the Dutch *Veldesch-doorn*, but in Denmark it is *navr*, and in Sweden *naverlönn*. It is found wild throughout central Europe, but not in the northern regions. Exceptionally, it makes a really big tree; there is one eighty-six feet tall at Cobham Hall in Kent, and another twelve feet round at Pampisford in Cambridgeshire.

The Norway maple is another tree that has a resemblance to a sycamore, but closer study reveals several clear points of difference. It has a brown bark on both trunk and twigs, and its opposite buds are distinctly red (p. 43). The five-lobed leaves have a sharply angled outline, not rounded as in the sycamore, and each lobe and notch ends in an angular point. The leaves show beautiful rust-red tints when they open in April, and pleasing golden ones when they fall in October— colours not seen on sycamore. The flowers differ both in arrangement and time of appearance. They open in April, just ahead of the leaves, as golden-yellow clusters with red bracts beneath; each flower spike stands erect and does not droop (Plate 25). The seeds are set at a less acute angle to each other than those of the sycamore, and are flatter. The leafy tissues, if cut, exude a white milky-sap. The wood is white and strong, and has the same uses as sycamore, but because Norway maple does not make such a large tree it is seldom planted for timber production.

**Norway Maple**
Leaves with acute lobes and points

As its name suggests, Norway maple grows wild in Scandinavia, and also across most of northern Europe. It was introduced to Britain in the seventeenth century, and has been widely and deservedly planted as a decorative tree. It bears seed freely, and has become naturalized in many woodlands. The seed sprouts eighteen months after falling. In France the Norway maple is called *erable plane*, while the Germans call it *Spitzahorn*, or pointed maple from the shape of its leaf. In Holland it is called *Noorsche eschdoorn*, in Sweden *lönn* and in Norway and Denmark *løn* or *spidsløn*. Our tallest, eighty-one feet, is at Pampisford near Cambridge, and our stoutest, thirteen and a half feet round, at Glendurgan, Cornwall. The scientific name is *Acer platanaides*.

This tree is occasionally tapped in Europe for maple sugar, which is obtained by driving a spout into the trunk in spring, just before the leaves break. The tree is then mobilizing its food reserves to support fresh growth of springwood (see p. 3) and leaves, and sap rising from the roots is in fact a strong sugar solution which flows freely. The sap must be concentrated the same day as it is gathered in order to give a thick syrup or a solid candy, otherwise it ferments and goes sour, so it is boiled in an iron pan over a fire of logs.

In North America there are many kinds of maple, and the maple leaf has been chosen as Canada's national emblem. All show fine autumn colouring, becoming golden, orange or scarlet. One, the Sugar maple, *Acer saccharum*, is tended commercially in New England as a source of syrup and candy. The only one widely planted in Britain is the Silver-leaf maple, *A. saccharinum*, which bears a sharply-toothed leaf with an attractive silvery undersurface.

The Japanese maple, *A. palmatum*, is nowadays widely grown in a great variety of decorative cultivars. Most of these have red foliage in various shades, and their leaves are often deeply divided so that they appear palmately compound and not merely lobed. The autumn colours are surprisingly brilliant in many kinds. These cultivars have been selected over the centuries by discerning Japanese gardeners, and are increased by grafting. Many are bushy forms, and this maple is also a favourite tree for the craft of *bonsai*, or the growing of miniature trees.

# Laburnum

*Laburnum anagyroides*                    Leguminoseae

In May the little laburnum tree becomes a glorious sight, displaying its hanging blossoms in cascades of gold. Because it flowers so freely year after year, and never grows too large for its surroundings, it has long been favoured for planting in

**Laburnum in bloom**
A, seed-pod

streets and town gardens, and happily it has great tolerance of dust and smoke (Plate 26). Laburnum was introduced to Britain from southern Europe at some unrecorded date, earlier than the sixteenth century. It is now quite at home here and occasionally spreads by self-sown seed.

Every feature of this tree is distinctive. Its twigs are greyish green and the buds, which are alternately placed, are clothed with silvery hairs (p. 44). The bark is a peculiar olive green, becoming brown and then dark grey on old trunks; it is smooth with prominent pores. Laburnum is the only common tree with a trifoliate compound leaf, consisting of three leaflets on a long stalk; they are clothed in grey hairs on their undersides. It is also the only common tree with showy yellow flowers; these have the typical form of the sweet-pea family and are borne in long hanging chains of about thirty blossoms apiece, with the youngest at the tip. Each flower has five sepals and five petals, with ten stamens that are joined towards their base to form a tube—a peculiar feature that the laburnum shares with the broom. The single-celled pistil ripens by late autumn into a dark brown, almost black pod, containing many small, hard, shiny black seeds. As the pod dries, it twists and breaks apart into two halves, scattering the seeds within; they are considered poisonous, both to children and livestock.

Seedling laburnums have at first two oval, hairless seed-leaves, which are followed by normal trifoliate leaves. They are grown mainly as stocks on to which nurserymen's varieties may be grafted. Besides the common species, gardeners grow the so-called Scotch laburnum, *L. alpinum*, from the mountains of southern Europe; it has longer chains of flowers and a winged seed-pod. Some of the decorative strains arose as hybrids between the two species. The roots, like those of other leguminous plants, bear nodules in which bacteria 'fix' the nitrogen of the air.

Laburnum has a dead-white sapwood and a dark orange-brown heartwood which is attractive, strong, and naturally durable. Though the tree is so small, it has been widely used for turnery, wood-carving, and inlay work, also for furniture and musical instruments. Because of the heartwood's resemblance to ebony, the French call the whole tree *faux ebenier* or false ebony, but more usually *cytise*. The German name, based more poetically on the flowers, is *Goldregen*, golden rain, and the tree is often called 'golden rain' or 'golden chain' in England also. In Wales the laburnum is called *euron*, golden (tree) or *tres aur*, chains of gold. The name laburnum was used by the Romans, apparently for this tree. In Irish it is *labran*.

# Locust

*Robinia pseudacacia*                              LEGUMINOSEAE

This striking tree puzzled the settlers who found it in the eastern states of America, being something entirely new. Because it bears seed in pods, they gave it the biblical name of 'locust', and this has remained its general name throughout the United States. The 'locust' of the Bible was probably the carob bean, *Ceratonia siliqua*, which bears edible seed-pods. After specimens were brought to Europe in 1601 the tree was called *Robinia* in honour of Jean Robin, the French botanist who introduced it; hence it is known as *robinier* in France, and as *Robinie* in Germany and Scandinavia, also as 'robinia' in England. As there are spines at the base of each leaf, it is also called 'acacia' or 'false-acacia', the latter being the '*pseud-acacia*' of its scientific name, and the *faux-acacier* of the French.

Locust is easily known by its pale green leaf, which opens in May and is alternately set and pinnately compound, and up to a foot long. The numerous leaflets, twenty-one or so, are oval. At the base of each leaf there are two sharp spines, which are actually modified stipules, a feature found on no other common tree (p. 44). These spines also make recognition of the winter twig certain. The buds are very small and scarcely visible.

The flowers, borne in June, are both beautiful and distinctive, consisting of hanging clusters of fragrant white blossoms, each like a little sweet-pea flower. They have the typical shape of the great family Leguminoseae. There are five green sepals, then five peculiar petals, namely a 'standard' at the back, two 'wings' on either side, and two 'keel' petals united to form a boat-shaped 'keel' at the front. All this ensures that a visiting bee must follow a fixed path on her way to gather

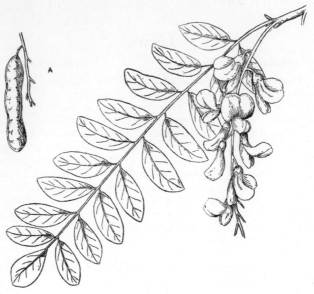

**Locust in flower**
A, seed-pod

nectar, and the five stamens are curved in the keel to dust her back with pollen, which is transferred to the one-celled pistil of another flower. The fruits, which ripen by October, are long, thin, dark brown pods, which open to release many small, round, hard black seeds during the winter.

Locust seeds often lie dormant for eighteen months. The

seedling bears in turn two oval seed-leaves, a few simple leaves,
then leaves with few leaflets; normal compound leaves follow.
If a locust tree is felled the stump sends up coppice shoots with
great vigour; sucker shoots also spring up from its roots.
Once you have a locust tree, it is very hard to get rid
of it!

The bark is a useful aid to identifying the locust; it is pale
brown in colour and has a network of ridges thicker than those
of any other broadleaved tree (Plate 28). The form of the
grown tree is pleasing to the eye (Plate 27), but very unsatis-
factory from the timber merchant's angle for the trunk is
fluted and irregular in cross section, and seldom straight for
more than a few feet together. The Americans, either handling
bigger trees or working small ones with hand tools, have found
it a useful timber, but as grown in Europe it is seldom better
than firewood. Though the form of the tree is so poor, being
often snake-like, the wood itself has good properties: the
sapwood is pale yellow and the heartwood golden-brown with
a shiny surface. As the heartwood is durable it is used in
America for fence stakes, and all the wood is valued for
attractive furniture and turned woodware, including tool
handles.

The roots of the locust bear curious nodules in which lives
a bacterium, *Bacterium radicis*, which enables the tree to 'fix'
nitrogen from the air. This is a feature of the plants and trees
of the family Leguminoseae, but is found in few others. It
helps the locust to grow on very poor soils, and therefore it is
sometimes planted on slag heaps, mainly in order to screen
them. On the Continent it has been more widely planted for
this purpose, also for soil fixation and as a source of firewood
and small poles. It has also become naturalized. About the
year 1823, the writer William Cobbett, author of *Rural Rides*,
advocated its planting for timber in England; many landowners
followed his advice, and their successors have been trying to
sell the trees ever since! The locust's real place with us is as
an ornamental specimen on the lawn of a large park where it

looks truly magnificent. There is a tree ninety-nine feet high at Bowood in Wiltshire, and one sixteen feet round at Grey-court School in Surrey.

# Blackthorn, Bullace and Plums

*Prunus* species                    ROSACEAE

These three trees, all with plum-like fruits, introduce us to the large natural family Rosaceae, founded by botanists on the characters of the common wild rose, *Rosa canina*. Features that all members of the Rose family have in common are found in their flowers, namely: a united calyx of five green petals; a corolla of five petals, each standing free from its neighbours; a cluster of numerous free stamens; and a pistil with from one to five cells, placed above the other flower members. All have gay, showy flowers which bear nectar and attract the insects that effect most of the pollination, though a good deal of the pollen is wind-borne also.

Many genera are included in the Rose family, but here we deal only with those that include trees. Each genus is distinguished, in part at least, by its fruit. The genus *Prunus* is based on the plum tree, in fact *prunus* is the Latin name for plum and the source of our word 'prune' for dried plums. The technical name for a plum is a 'drupe', and it consists of three layers: a tough outer skin (exocarp); a fleshy middle layer (mesocarp); and a single hard stone-like seed (endocarp). Because it is formed by the swelling of the carpel which stands above the other parts of the flower, it is free from the traces of the calyx found on some other fruits of this family.

The genus *Prunus* is itself a big one, divided into sections. The plums and their near allies form the section Prunoidae, which is distinguished by deciduous leaves, smooth fruit stones, and flowers borne singly or in small groups, not in large clusters like those of the cherries.

## Blackthorn

Blackthorn is our commonest wild plum, growing in hedge-rows and on waste land throughout the British Isles and across northern Europe. Its botanical name of *Prunus spinosa*, thorny plum, is derived from its vicious black thorns. There are three kinds of twigs: long ones which extend growth; short spurs that bear leaves, flowers and fruit, but grow outwards extremely slowly; and the spines or thorns, which begin as short shoots bearing leaves but end in a sharp woody point. Their purpose is to protect the tree from browsing animals, and even when they die they stay in place and act as effective defenders. The winter twigs are black, except for the long shoots which are crimson on one side and green on the other. The buds are alternately set, small, oval and bluntly pointed (p. 48); they are reddish to purplish-black. On old trees the black bark becomes broken into small square plates. If scratched, it reveals purple or orange-red tints. The wood has a pale yellow sapwood and a tough dark brown heart. It is too small for general use, but it provides knobbly walking sticks and cudgels, being the traditional timber for the Irish shillelagh. It was once widely used for hay-rake teeth and the swingles of flails—the part that is banged against the grain during threshing.

Blackthorn is usually seen as a hedgerow shrub (Plate 29). It is very aggressive and if left alone spreads out across fields by means of sucker shoots springing up from its roots. The resulting blackthorn thicket often protects the unarmed saplings of other trees from damage by animals, so helping in the formation of taller woodland. Fruit growers sometimes use blackthorn suckers as rootstocks for the grafting of choicer plums. Bushes often form an effective part of a stockproof hedge, but only by chance, for the blackthorn is seldom so planted. It can grow up to twenty feet tall, with a trunk two feet round. On wild hillsides in the west it often forms thickets, impenetrable by reason of its spines and close, irregular branching. It is equally at home on soils rich in lime or lacking it.

Blackthorn flowers early, towards the end of March and just after the spring equinox, when day-length equals night-length. In a cold, late spring its leaves are still unopened, and the masses of snow-white flowers on black branches are a striking sight. But in a warm, early spring its tender green leaves are already open, giving an attractive, though less vivid combination of colour. The leaves are small with toothed edges, oval and pointed, and carried on short crimson-green stalks (p. 36).

The fruit ripens through green to a lustrous purplish-black globe, about half an inch long, covered with a white waxy bloom (Plate 59). The flesh within is pale green, and the stone is brown. Though it looks fully ripe in October, this sloe, as the blackthorn 'plum' is called, is still very acid to the taste. After the first frosts it sweetens a little, and some people find raw sloes palatable. Most of us prefer to add plenty of sugar to turn them into sloe jelly; or to ferment sloe wine. If pickled in spirit they provide sloe gin. Most sloes are picked by birds who eat the flesh and drop the stone, apparently without swallowing it. It then lies dormant where it falls for eighteen months. The seedling sends up two thick oval seed-leaves, and normal leaves follow.

Blackthorn is remarkable for having two names in several languages, one for the tree and one for the fruit. The tree name usually means 'black thorn'. In German it is *Schwarzdorn* and *Schlehe*, in Dutch *sleedoren* and *sleepruim*. In Scotland the tree is *slaethorn* and the fruits *slaes* or *bullisters* (from bullace). The French call it *épine noire* and *prunellier;* the Welsh *draenen du* and *eirinen;* while Irish names are *draigean dub* (in Gaelic *draighean dubh*) and *har*. The Danes call it *slåen*, and the Norwegians *slåpetorn*.

### Bullace

The bullace, which grows wild in hedgerows in the south of England and central Europe, and is cultivated in regions farther north, differs from the blackthorn in the following points: its bark is brown, not black; the twigs are straighter and less spiny; the leaves are larger, broader, more coarsely toothed and downy on the underside; the flowers are larger, with broader petals; the fruit, which may be black or yellow, droops and is from three-quarters to one inch in diameter.

The name 'bullace' and the Welsh *bulas* come from French *beloce*. The scientific name is *Prunus insititia;* the latter word means 'grafted', but has no significance here. In Germany this wild plum is distinguished as *Schlehenpflaume*, or sloe-plum, while in Denmark it is called *kræge*. Many kinds of plums, including damsons, greengages, and mirabelles, are derived in whole or part from the bullace. It is used as a rootstock for grafting plums of all kinds.

## Wild Plums

Orchard plums often give rise to 'escaped' trees that spring up from plum-stones dropped by birds or people along the hedgerows. These trees, which may be found anywhere in the British Isles, can be distinguished from the blackthorn and the bullace by their spineless twigs, which are also hairless. Their flowers are larger and tend to be less numerous, being often set in pairs (Plate 30). Their fruits are larger and more luscious, and vary in colour from yellow to red, purple and black. Exact description is not possible, because of their varied ancestry. The domestic plums themselves are derived from the bullace, from the 'wild plum' of the species *Prunus domestica*, which has brown twigs, and from the Cherry plum, *P. cerasifera*, also called the myrobalan, which is distinguished by its green twigs. The two latter trees come from the Near East; *domestica* means 'tame' while *cerasifera* means 'cherry-bearing.'

Plums of one kind or another have been grown, or at least appreciated in Britain from very early times. Sloe stones were found at the Glastonbury Lake village, occupied in the Bronze

7

Age, and plum stones have been unearthed at many Roman settlements. The word 'plum', allied to the German *Pflaume* and the Danish *blomme*, is found in the names of Anglo-Saxon villages such as Plumstead in Kent. Today the big plum-growing areas are Kent and Worcestershire. Each named variety is a clone, grafted on to a common stock.

Plum trees have a smooth, dark brown, or purplish-black, bark, and often reach a height of thirty feet with a girth of three feet. Their oval leaves have toothed edges and a well-marked network of veins, and often bear two little glands close to the stalk. The leaf stalk is often crimson rather than green, and has two stipules—tiny narrow leaflets—at its base. The winter buds are pointed and show many scales, and on the short shoots, which bear the flowers and fruit, they are clustered together. The flowers, always white though sometimes with a greenish tinge, are often paired. They open in April at about the same time as the leaves, and the fruit ripens in August. The hard flattish stone of the plum is pale brown, whatever the colour of the flesh may be, and has a prominent rib where its two halves join. The kernel within is edible. When the seed germinates next spring, two fleshy oval cotyledons are raised above ground. The hedgerow 'wild' plums arise in this way, whereas orchard ones are always grafted. The roots of both send up sucker shoots freely.

Plum wood has a pale yellow sapwood zone, and a distinctive violet-brown to pinkish-brown heart. On the Continent it is valued for decorative veneers, inlaid work and wood carving; but in Britain it is used mainly as firewood which burns with a fruity fragrance. Wounded stems exude a sweet gum. In France the plum tree is called *prunier*. *Zwetschge* is one German name. Other names have been mentioned earlier, under plum or blackthorn.

### Copper-leaved Plum

In 1880 Monsieur Pissart, gardener to the Shah of Persia, sent home to Paris specimens of an unusual decorative tree

(Plate 36). This was named in his honour *Prunus cerasifera* variety *pissardi*, and under the trade name of *Prunus* 'pissardi' it is now widely raised and sold by nurserymen. All of us know it as a garden and street tree of small size and handsome appearance, but many people confuse it with the copper beech. The Copper-leaved plum, however, has a jet black, roughish bark quite unlike that of any beech tree. Its small leaves are at first reddish-brown, then copper-coloured and eventually purplish-brown, but the shades vary with the strain. They are borne on coppery shoots, and have toothed-edges—unlike the smooth-edged leaf of beech. The flowers, which open with the leaves in April, are white with a pinkish tinge, and the small plums are purple.

## Cherries

*Prunus* species                                    ROSACEAE

Within the genus *Prunus* (p. 84), the cherries form the sections *Cerasus* and *Padus* which are distinguished by decidu-ous leaves and their habit of bearing flowers in groups, rather than singly. Two native kinds will be described here, and two introduced sorts. There are many other species, hybrids, and cultivars which give us delightful flowers in the spring, or delicious fruits in the autumn. The *Cerasus* cherries bear their flowers in umbels, while the *Padus* cherries have their flowers in racemes or spikes.

### Gean

The gean or Common wild cherry, *Prunus avium*, of the section *Cerasus*, is a magnificent tree found sparingly in mixed woodlands over most of Britain and Ireland (Plate 31). It is one of the few trees to flourish with the beech on chalk hills in the south. Its bark is very distinctive, having prominent horizontal bands of pores or lenticels, forming orange-brown corky ridges on an otherwise smooth and polished surface (Plate 33). Often the bark breaks away in horizontal strips.

Its general colour is purplish-grey to violet-brown. The winter buds are alternate, brown and pointed, with many scales. On the short shoots, which bear leaves and flowers but grow longer only slowly, the buds are clustered (p. 49). When the leaves open in April they show attractive bronzy-brown tints, but soon change to pale green. In autumn they fade to purplish

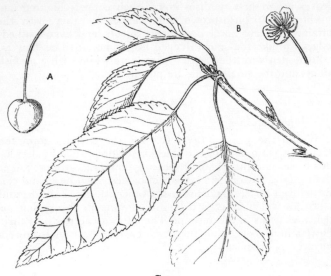

**Gean**
A, fruit; B, flower

or crimson shades before they fall. Each leaf is elliptical in outline, with a long stalk, a toothed edge and a pointed tip. As a rule the leaves droop from the branches. A curious feature is the presence of two glands on the leaf stalk, near the leaf-blade.

The cherry tree bursts into flower in May, just after the

leaves come out (Plate 34). The blossoms open in clusters near the tips of the branches, so abundantly that the whole tree appears to be smothered in snow. Each cluster holds from two to six flowers which spring from the twig on long, individual stalks. Each flower consists of a calyx-cup of five united sepals, five large, white, free petals, about twenty-five golden stamens and a single-celled pistil. Nectar is secreted within the heart of the flower, which is pollinated by insects. Orchard cherries are a valued source of honey for the beekeeper.

Gean fruits ripen early, about July, changing from green to dark red and sometimes to black. They have a leathery outer skin, a thin sweet pulp, and a large woody seed. Though they are not very rewarding to people, birds eat them greedily and later void the seeds, so spreading the tree. Bird-sown gean seeds probably germinate next spring, but if the cherries are gathered by man they must be stored in moist sand for twenty-one months before they will sprout. The seedling sends up two oval, fleshy seed-leaves, and the first true leaves are oppositely placed; alternate leaves follow.

The gean yields a beautiful timber. Its sapwood is pale yellow with a greenish tinge. The heartwood is golden-brown, again with a hint of green, a lively pattern of grain, and a gleaming surface. Large trunks are valued for veneers to decorate high-class furniture. Smaller limbs are used for wood-carving and turnery, such as fruit bowls, again for choice work. Branchwood makes a wonderful firewood, which burns well and fills the room with a rich perfume. If the growing tree is wounded, a clear yellow sticky gum oozes out to seal the wound. This gum is full of sugar and is sweet to the taste, and it was once used by doctors to soften the taste of sour medicines.

Though not one of our largest trees, gean often keeps pace with beech and oak; the tallest, at Woburn, Bedfordshire, scales 102 feet; the stoutest, at Elvetham in Hampshire, is twelve feet round. Gean is frequently planted by landowners who wish to ornament their woods and grow, at the same time, a readily marketable timber. It is nearly always so used in mixture with other broadleaved trees. Coppice shoots spring freely from stumps of felled geans.

The gean is the main source, or at least one of the sources of most orchard cherries, and its lofty habit explains why these are so hard to keep pruned down to a reasonable height. Cultivated kinds are distinguished by thicker pulp, and may be white, red or black. The main centres of commercial growing are Kent and Worcestershire. Grass is grown below the trees, and is grazed by sheep. A double form, in which a second set of petals is formed by converted stamens, is grown in gardens; it is increased, like the fruiting varieties, by grafting on a common stock, usually of ordinary gean. As a wild tree the gean is found right across Europe as far north as Denmark. Cultivated strains are of course grown in every temperate country of the world.

'Gean', pronounced with a hard 'g', was originally the Low Latin name *guina*. This was applied to a strain of cherries cultivated in France as *guignes*, which were taken to Scotland and called *guinds*. Eventually this name was applied to wild trees also, and in its modern form 'gean' was adopted in England. 'Mazard', another name, comes from Old French *merisard*, allied to modern French *merisier*, though the French also call the tree *cerisier*.

The generic name *Prunus* means a plum; *avium* means 'of the birds', for although the gean is not the 'bird cherry' in Britain, Linnaeus knew it as 'bird-berry' in his native Sweden. Most other names resemble Latin *cerasus*, a cherry, being in France *cerisier*, in Germany *Kirsche*, in Holland *kers*, in Wales *ceiriosen* and *sirianen* and in Scandinavia *kirs*. The Gaelic is *sirist*, and the Irish *sirir* and *seilin*. The wild tree is distinguished in German as *Vogel Kirsche*, in Danish as *fugle kirsebaer;* and in Sweden as *faagelbär*, because of its associations with the birds. 'Kirsch' is of course the name of a liqueur flavoured with cherries, which also give us cherry brandy, as well as jams, preserves and dessert fruits.

## Sour Cherry

The Sour cherry or Morello, *Prunus cerasus*, of the section *Cerasus*, is found naturalized as an escape from orchards in most European countries. Its original home was probably in Asia Minor, and it is one of the sources of many cultivated

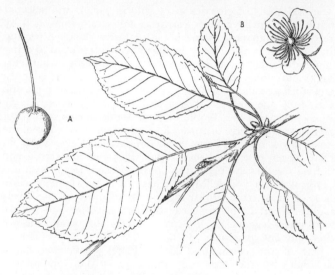

**Sour Cherry**
A, fruit; B, flower

kinds. Its fruits are purplish-red in colour and are somewhat sour, hence its name, also *Sauerkirsche* in Germany and *surkirsebær* in Denmark. The sour cherry is distinguished from the gean by other small features. Its leaves are bluish-green and have round-toothed edges; their stalks lack glands. The flower is cup-shaped and the petals are slightly notched. The sour cherry is never more than a small tree. Unlike the gean it is very apt to send up sucker shoots from its roots—a habit shared by garden cherries that have been grafted on a Morello stock.

## Japanese Cherries

Several kinds of cherries grow wild in Japan, and selected strains of them have been grown as cultivars, propagated by grafting, in Japanese gardens for centuries. Many flowering kinds of great ornamental value have been introduced to other temperate countries and are now a familiar sight in gardens, parks, and along roadsides. As a rule they are grafted on a gean stock just above ground level; hence the bark of the trunk is that of the special strain, and is sometimes strikingly handsome. Most are double or semi-double forms grown for their riotous displays of spring flowers which often conceal the leaves below them. Few of these double forms ever set fruit. They flower so freely because their blossoms are sterile and no food reserves are needed to nourish a seed. If you examine a typical flower you will find it has few or no stamens, since most of them have grown into petals to produce the lovely double flower. In place of a pistil there are often one or two small green leaflets. Such a tree is a freak that would die out after only one generation in the wild.

One of the commonest kinds (Plate 37) is that called 'Kanzan' by the Japanese, after one of their mountains. Botanically, it is the cultivar 'Sekiyama' (the name of another mountain) of the wild species *Prunus serrulata*, of the *Cerasus* section. It has a violet-brown bark with prominent orange lenticels in horizontal bands, and a metallic lustre. The leaves are bronze when they unfold, while in autumn they assume tints of yellow and crimson. The flowers, produced in profusion on numerous short spurs, are a vivid pinkish-mauve with double petals which soon fall in showers after their brief spell of glory. Other well-known cultivars are 'Hi-sakura', with single blossoms, and 'Ama-no-gawa', which grows erect as a

slender bush, clothed in flowers to its foot. The Japanese name
for cherries as a group is *sakura*.

### Bird Cherry

The native Bird cherry, *Prunus padus*, differs from the kinds
previously described, in bearing its flowers in a long hanging
chain or raceme (Plate 38), a feature of the section *Padus*. In
Scotland, Ireland, the north of England and throughout
Wales it is found as a small bushy tree, often along streamsides; but in the south of England it is rare, except in cultivation. On the Continent it is a northern or mountain species.
Its bark is quite different to that of common cherries, being
black and broken up into numerous small square patches; if
rubbed, it smells of bitter almonds. The wood too differs;
there is a white sapwood and a dark, purplish-brown heart.
The leaves are smaller than those of cultivated cherries, and
have a smooth, shining surface. The tree can reach a height of
forty feet, and a girth of four feet.

The bird cherry flowers in June and is then an exceptionally
pretty sight, displaying chains of dainty white flowers against
a curtain of dark green foliage. The berries, which ripen in
August, are a glossy jet-black. They are too small and sour for
people to eat, but as the tree's name suggests, the birds love
them.

In Scotland this tree is called hag-cherry, from the Norse
name *hegg*, allied to Swedish *hägg* and Danish *hœgg*. This word,
applied now to the tree, once meant the fruit; it has nothing
to do with hedges, since it was used before hedges were
planted. The German name is *Traubenkirsche*, and the French
is *cerisier à grappes*, both meaning bunch-flowered cherry.

## Almond

*Prunus amygdalus*                                    ROSACEAE

This beautiful little tree is very widely planted for the
surprising beauty of its bright pink blossoms which open on

bare twigs very early in the spring (Plate 39). Sometimes they appear before February is over, and they are usually out by March. As they fade the leaves open, at first bright green and later a deeper green that persists through the summer. Even when leafless the almond is easily known. As a rule it has an open crown of rather level branches. The twigs are green below, but show a peculiar purplish-crimson colour on their upper sides where they catch the sunlight. The small brown buds are alternately set, and often hairy (p. 50). The almond leaf is distinctive: its stalk has two stipules at its foot, and there are two glands at the actual leaf base; the leaf blade is lance-shaped and remarkably long, with a slightly toothed edge and a long narrow point; the glossy dark green upper surface marks it out.

The pink flowers are set singly, but appear so freely that the whole branch appears aglow with bloom. Each has five sepals, five petals, many stamens, and a one-celled pistil, arising from a crimson-tinted base. Their abundant nectar and pollen attract the earliest bees. The fruit that follows is oval, with a tough, leathery, rough-surfaced, pale green outer skin, and no sweet pulp at all. The stone has a tough, woody, pale brown shell, pitted with peculiar holes. It falls out when the green casing opens, and its distribution in nature appears to depend on seed-eating birds or rodents who lose some of the almonds that they gather. The shell must be cracked with considerable force before its kernel—the familiar almond of commerce—can be obtained. This almond, which is actually the two seed-leaves, has a rough dark brown skin and a hard creamy flesh which is both nutritious and delicious to the taste. In nature the unopened whole seed lies for one winter in the soil; when it sprouts the seed-leaves remain below ground within the husk and only a shoot appears—a mode of germination different to that of plums and cherries.

The peculiar flavour of almonds—relished in almond paste or marzipan—is due to minute amounts of hydrocyanic acid, also called prussic acid. In some strains, grown abroad, the concentration is dangerous, and though they are used for their 'bitter almonds' flavouring, they cannot be eaten raw in any quantity. In Britain almond trees fruit sparingly and have no commercial value, but great quantities of almonds are imported from Mediterranean lands.

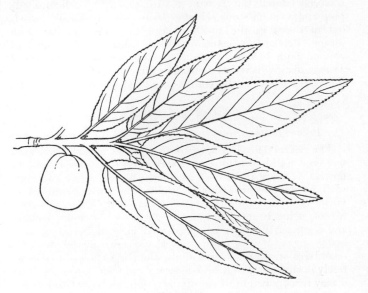

**Almond**
Leaves and fruit

Almond bark, at first smooth, later develops clear, horizontal bands of rough-edged breathing pores. Its colour, a slaty purple, is most unusual. The wood has a pale yellow sapwood zone, and a dark violet-brown heart, being one of the few bluish woods.

The almond is native to western Asia, but has long been

cultivated in southern Europe. It reached Britain about the sixteenth century where it is grown only for ornament, being grafted on a plum stock. The word 'almond' is based on the French *amande*, the tree being *amandier;* the German equivalents are *Mandel* and *Mandelbaum*. The peach, *Prunus persica*, is closely related, but its fruit is distinguished by delicious soft pulp and a rough stone. Hardy strains are occasionally grown out of doors in the south of England. Though its name means 'Persian', it came originally from China. Peach and almond both belong to the *Amygdalus* section of the genus *Prunus*, distinguished by a pitted or furrowed stone. *Amygdalos*, the Greek name, is the source of all the names for almonds.

## Cherry Laurel

*Prunus laurocerasus*                                    ROSACEAE

The cherry laurel is seen more often as a bush than as a tree, and its identity puzzles many people because it seldom flowers. It is apt to be confused with the Sweet bay and even with rhododendrons, though unlike the rhododendrons it grows vigorously on chalk soils. A native of Greece and Asia Minor, it has been introduced to all parts of Britain, Ireland and northern Europe, being planted in shrubberies or as a hedge shrub. If it is clipped back, or grown in the shade of taller trees, it will not flower. Only where it is allowed to spread freely in sunlight will it bear blossom and fruit. Growing thus, it may reach a height of twenty feet, with a woody trunk three feet round.

The evergreen leaves of the cherry laurel are elliptical in shape, broadening towards the tip and then narrowing to a blunt point (Plate 40). They are a glossy mid-green above and pale green below, and if you crush them they give out a faint but inescapable smell of almonds. This odour, their colour, and their shape distinguish them from other evergreen shrubs with alternately placed leaves; they stand moreover on very short green stalks. The almond-like smell comes from the weak fumes of hydrocyanic (or prussic) acid, found in the leaf. These fumes are poisonous and entomologists use crushed cherry laurel leaves to kill insects without damaging them as specimens, by placing both leaves and insect together in a closed glass tube.

**Cherry Laurel**
Evergreen leaves and black cherries

When the cherry laurel flowers it sends up a slender spike of white blossoms, each with the typical cherry form. They have a distinct odour and bear ample nectar. The fruits, which ripen in October, are small black cherries, quite good to eat, but they are soon stripped from the tree by the birds.

The bark is black, with a rough surface composed of many small squarish panels. The wood within has a white sap-wood and a dark purplish-brown heart, but it is seldom large enough for anything except firewood.

Cherry laurel is grown mainly as a shelter bush for garden walks, or as cover for pheasants on large estates. Its foliage has a commercial value for use by florists, and is widely used in flower arrangements. Its specific name, *laurocerasus*, means 'laurel cherry', and so does its German name, *Kirschlorbeer*, and its French one, *laurier cerisier*. With other evergreen species, it forms the section *Laurocerasus* of the genus *Prunus*.

# Wild Pear

*Pyrus communis*                                    ROSACEAE

The wild pear is an uncommon tree with a slender spire-like form and a rough bark broken into squares, thicker than those of the crab apple. It is a taller and stouter tree, reaching fifty feet high by eight feet round (Plate 41). Some, though not all the twigs bear long sharp brown spines which distinguish wild pears from cultivated ones. The leaf can be distinguished by its remarkably long stalk which often exceeds the length of the blade and is longer, in proportion, than that of any common tree. The blade is oval to heart-shaped, and has a smooth, shining, dark green upper surface, and a short fine point. The flowers differ from those of apple in appearing before the leaves are open, and in being wholly white, not tinged with pink. They have five sepals, five petals, many stamens and a five-celled pistil.

Pear fruits can always be told apart from apples by the absence of any hollows around the stalk, and by their typical 'pear' shape which results from the stalk end being narrower than the tip. They are also peculiar in having 'grit cells' in their pulp, which give the fruit its gritty texture. The wild pear is green at first, ripening to dull brown. It remains woody and sour for a long time, becoming just sweet enough to eat after the first hard frosts. Birds peck it as it softens, and swallow or scatter the pips, which are brown or black; these sprout next spring, raising two seed-leaves above ground. Bird-sown pears turn up in odd places, and persist longer in woods than wild apples because they grow taller.

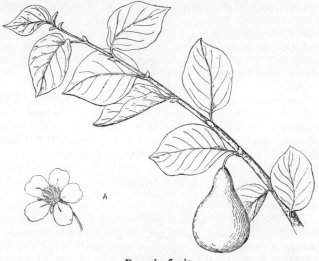

**Pear in fruit**
A, flower

Pear wood, also called 'fruitwood', is large enough for commercial use for small objects. It has a warm purplish red colour and is very stable. It finishes with a soft smooth surface. Before plastics were developed it was widely used for drawing instruments, such as set-squares; it makes good trays and turned objects, and sculptors employ it for wood carving. It is also used in pattern making. It burns well. Pear bark is brownish-grey and rough and breaks up into distinct squares (Plate 42); buds are shown on p. 49.

As with the apples, there are many pear cultivars suited to particular uses such as dessert pears, cooking pears, and pears for fermenting to the alcoholic drink called perry, popular in south-west England.

*Pyrus*, spelt *pirus*, was the Roman name for this tree, and the specific name, *communis*, means common. Nearly all European names resemble *pyrus;* in France the fruit is *poire*, the tree *poirier;* the Dutch is *peer;* the German *Birne;* the Norwegian and Danish *paere*, and the Swedish *paron*. Gaelic *peur*, Irish *peirin* and Welsh *peiran* are related, but the generally used Welsh word *rhwningen* must come from some other, older source.

The natural range of the wild pear includes Ireland, Wales, England and western Europe. Cultivated kinds are grown in all temperate countries. A rare race, the Thorny pear, *Pyrus cordata*, which is very spiny and has heart-shaped leaf-bases, grows wild in Devon and Cornwall.

# Crab Apples

*Malus* species                                            ROSACEAE

The common wild apple or crab can be found in all parts of Britain and Ireland, and the neighbouring countries of Europe. It is the parent, in part at least, of the many delicious cultivated kinds, which are all cultivars or clones, propagated by grafting on the common stock. The wild race forms a bushy, much-branched tree (Plate 45) with sharp brown spines on some, though not all of its twigs. The bark on old stems is greyish-brown and breaks up into thin squarish plates (Plate 46). The wood is red-brown. It burns well but is too small and irregular for use as timber, except for ornamental carving; it is very tough, and countrymen sometimes use it for mallet heads, cudgels, or walking-sticks. The tree is rarely more than thirty feet high and three feet round. It has three sorts of shoots, long ones that extend its crown, short ones that bear flowers, and spines.

Several features that distinguish the wild tree will also help you to tell cultivated apples from other trees in orchards. The winter buds, which are alternate, have hairy scales and are small and pointed; the twigs are hairy too (p. 50). The leaves are simple and oval, with a toothed edge and a stalk of moderate length, and are bluntly pointed; their veins link up near the leaf edges (p. 36). The flowers open in late April just as the leaves do, and their pinkish colour marks them out; they grow in clusters, each on its own stalk (Plate 43). Each has five green sepals, five white petals tinged at the tip with rose-pink, many stamens and a five-celled pistil. The fruit (Plate 44) is formed by the swelling of the flower base into a sphere about one and a half inches across; it is called a 'pome', and its flesh holds five cells lined with a hard green papery coating, in each of which one or more seeds—the apple pips—develop. Remains of the calyx are seen at the tip. There is always a hollow at the base, round the stalk, and this distinguishes apples from pears. The pips are oval, pointed, and have a shiny, tough black skin.

Crab apples are green at first, but turn brown by late October. As winter advances they fall from the tree and decay. Dispersal of the seed depends on their attraction for birds and animals, such as badgers, mice, squirrels and deer, who are bound to scatter and swallow pips as they munch, or carry away the apples. The seed sprouts next spring, sending up two oval seed-leaves first. But crab stocks for grafting are increased from root-shoots or cuttings because a particular clone is preferred for 'stock' as well as for 'scion'. Nearly all the wild trees you see are chance-sown in hedgerows, on waste ground or in woodland clearings.

The Common crab is now called *Malus sylvestris*, meaning wild apple. A scarcer kind, *M. pumila* or 'dwarf apple', which has downy shoots, leaves and fruit stalks, and is therefore called the Downy crab, is also recognized. It is more nearly allied to orchard apples and many specimens are 'escapes'.

*Malus* is the Roman name. The French call the fruit *pomme* and the tree *pommier*. All the other names in northern Europe

8

are linked to 'apple', being in Dutch *appel*, German *Apfel*, Danish *abild*, Norwegian *apal*, Swedish *apel*, Welsh *afalen*, Gaelic *ubhall* and Irish *ubaill*. 'Crab' comes from *skrabba*, an old Norse name for apples.

The fruit of the wild crab is too sour to be eaten raw, save in times of scarcity, though it yields a tasty jelly. Strains with larger and sweeter fruits have been cultivated in orchards since Saxon times; 'orchard' was originally '(w)ort-yard', the place where 'worts' or edible plants were grown. The countless cultivated strains fall into four groups with different uses: eating or dessert apples; cooking apples; crab apples grown for showy blossom and fruits; and cider apples, which yield small sour fruits that give a juice suitable for fermenting into an alcoholic drink—sweet or strong, according to taste—called cider or 'scrumpy'.

The size of the apple crop varies from year to year. During a good summer the tree builds up food reserves which are used for flower-buds in the following spring, resulting in a heavy fruit crop later; thus the hot sunny summer finds expression in fruit *fifteen* months after it occurs, always provided a sharp late frost has not intervened and killed the blossom. As the flowers arise on short shoots or spurs the annual pruning is aimed at promoting their welfare by opening and restraining the crown to let them get ample sunlight.

# Rowan, Wild Service Tree and Whitebeams

*Sorbus* species                                    ROSACEAE

Those trees that form the *Sorbus* genus of the great Rose family are easily known when they are in flower for they have showy, white, five-petalled blossoms set in clusters on stalks which branch repeatedly and are called by the botanists 'compound cymes'. These trees are all spineless, a feature that marks them out from the spiny hawthorns which have similar flower clusters. When in fruit their seeds distinguish them, being small and scattered in the pulp in several cells, whereas the hawthorns bear one to three large hard stones at the centre of the berry. The word *sorbus* is the Roman one for the True service tree, which yields an edible fruit and a drink like cider, which was praised by Virgil.

Though flowers and fruits are alike, these *Sorbus* trees have very dissimilar leaves. They range from compound, through lobed forms to simple oval ones. Every kind of intermediate shape is found, as a result of interbreeding or local variation, and one authority lists seventeen native kinds! Here we will describe the five common and fairly distinct species, though two of these may be hybrids.

### Rowan

The rowan is one of our most attractive trees, both in cultivation and the wilds (Plate 48). It is sometimes called the 'mountain ash' because of its compound leaf. It has no other connection with ash, but it grows higher on the mountains than any other tree does, appearing up to 2,500 feet above sea level on windswept crags where its seedlings can escape destruction from sheep and deer. Its leaves are pinnately compound, with about seven pairs of leaflets set along a central stalk, each leaflet having a markedly toothed edge. The leaves turn crimson in autumn. The winter buds, which like the leaves are alternately placed, are remarkably large and purple in colour; they are oval and pointed, and each of the several scales is fringed with pale grey hairs (p. 50). The bark is purplish-grey, smooth but clearly marked by bands of breathing pores. The sapwood is yellow and the heartwood purplish brown. As the rowan is rarely a large tree, seldom exceeding fifty feet tall or two feet round, it is rarely used for timber today. But in the past the crofters in treeless districts of Scotland and Ireland used tough rowan wood for furniture, tool handles and cart shafts. It burns well as firewood.

Rowan bears a wealth of white blossom every year in May (Plate 49). Its pistils have three free styles, and the resulting berries ripen rapidly, being large and green by July, and bright

scarlet or orange by August; the colour varies from one tree
to another. They attract the birds early in autumn and the
trees are soon stripped. Any berries that fall to the ground are
greedily eaten by pheasants and domestic fowls. Birds digest
the pulp and pass out the seeds, and it is believed that seeds
so treated sprout next spring. Badgers also eat the berries and

**Rowan in fruit**
A, portion of flower-cluster

void the seeds. Squirrels swallow the pulp and gnaw the seeds
also. If seed is needed for sowing, the berries have to be stored
in damp sand for eighteen months before the seed will sprout.
Each seed then sends up two seed-leaves, followed by simple
leaves with toothed edges, before the compound form of leaf
appears.

Bird dispersal takes the rowan to all sorts of places inaccessible to man. Seedlings often sprout from cliff faces, or even from the forks or hollows of large old trees. In cultivation it is now universally seen as a garden tree, welcome for its displays of blossom and fruit, and also because it never grows too large. The berries, if boiled with plenty of sugar, yield a tasty jelly which goes down well with roast lamb or venison; but they are too sour to be eaten raw.

Curious superstitions surround the rowan. Highland crofters firmly believed that it would keep away evil spirits and always planted a rowan close to their dwellings. Today, when so many crofts have been abandoned, their ruins are often revealed by a wind-beaten rowan, surviving among the stones amid the heather. 'Rowan' itself is a Norse word, allied to Norwegian *rogn*, Swedish *ronn* and Danish *røn*, and according to the Danish philologist Johan Lange, all these words are linked to 'rune', meaning 'magic'. The old Norse alphabet of runes arose as signs carved on rowan bark and wood.

The Latin name of this tree is *Sorbus aucuparia*, or 'fowlers' service tree', because the berries were used as bait in bird traps. The French *sorbier des oiseleurs* has the same meaning, while the German *Vogelbeerebaum* means bird-berry-tree. The Dutch name is *lijsterbes*. The Celtic names are inter-linked, being *cerddinen* in Wales, *caortainn* in Ireland, and *caorunn* in Scotland where many burns and hills, such as Meall nan Chaorunnaich in Perthshire, are named after this tree. *Luis* is another Gaelic name, while *criafalen*, meaning the harsh or coarse apple, is sometimes used in Wales. In Scotland the berries are sometimes called 'roddens' from the 'rodden-tree', apparently because of their reddish colour.

### Wild Service Tree

This beautiful small tree is a definite rarity, although it is native to a large area of England and the Welsh Borders, south of the Mersey and the Humber. It is seldom planted and seldom recognized, and is most likely to be found in patches of old woodland on rough ground that has never been cleared. The flowers and fruit follow the *Sorbus* pattern, but the leaves are distinct, being five-lobed like those of a maple (p. 34); but you can easily tell the Wild service from maple because the leaves are *alternate* and not opposite. Winter buds (p. 47) are oval and blunt, and show several round scales each with a narrow brown edge. Wild service bark is blue-grey and smooth at first, but later breaks into rough squares and looks just like that of hawthorn. The trunk has a whitish sapwood and a red-brown heart; it is tough, but too small for use. Occasional trees grow seventy feet tall by eight feet round.

Wild service flowers in May and ripens its fruits in August. They are soft, dull crimson-brown and sweet enough to eat, but with a gritty texture. They were once sold in Kentish markets as 'chequers berries' from the 'chequers tree', a name that may have arisen from the 'chequerboard' appearance of the square-flaked bark. The seeds are spread by birds; if gathered they rest for eighteen months before sprouting. The seedling has two blunt, oblong seed-leaves, then oval leaves with toothed edges before the lobed form appears.

'Wild service' is a botanist's name, based on a slight resemblance to the True service tree, *Sorbus domestica*, which grows in France (where it is called *cormier*) and bears edible berries. 'Service' comes from *cerevisia*, a Roman alcoholic drink made by fermenting grain and *Sorbus* berries. The Latin name, *S. torminalis*, and the Danish and Swedish *tarmvrid* (literally 'tummy-writhe') are based on the use of the berries to cure colic. The German name is *Elsbeere* and the French *alisier torminal*. This tree is found over Central Europe and in southern Scandinavia. In Wales it is called *cerddinen wyllt*, or 'strange rowan'.

### Whitebeams

The Common whitebeam, *Sorbus aria*, is one of the prettiest sights of spring when it opens its leaves in cup-shaped groups, glistening white below. This colour is due to a dense coating of white hairs, which lessen the loss of water by transpiration

on the dry, lime-rich soils which this tree prefers. The whiteness lasts all summer and can even be seen on faded, fallen
leaves which are brown on their upper side. It gives the tree
its name, 'beam' being a Saxon word for tree. In shape the
leaves are oval, with a short stalk, a pointed tip and a clearly

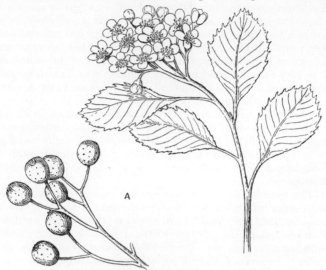

**Whitebeam in flower**
A, fruits

toothed edge. Their upper surface is mid-green. The winter
buds are noticeably large, oval, and pointed (p. 47). Their
clear green colour marks them out from those of rowan,
but the edge of each scale has a brown or purple rim. The
bark is greenish grey, and always remains smooth, even on old
trees. The wood has a pale yellow sapwood and a brown heart.
Though the tree is too small to be planted for timber, logs
are occasionally used for turnery or firewood.

Whitebeam flowers, which open in May, are large and white (Plate 47). The berries, ripening in August, are scarlet and make a brave show. They are too sour to eat, but they can be made into jelly. The birds spread the seeds, and young seedlings often spring up on waste ground. Under cultivation, seed needs storage for eighteen months; when it sprouts it shows two seed-leaves, then normal foliage. Whitebeam is never a big tree, the limits being about fifty feet tall and four feet round. It likes full light and is usually seen on woodland fringes or in hedgerows. On the chalk downs of the south-east it is very common, and it grows frequently on limestone soils throughout Britain and Ireland. On non-lime soils it turns up locally as far north as mid-Scotland.

The Welsh name is *criafalen wen*, or white rowan. In France the whitebeam is *alisier blanc*, and in Germany *Mehlbeere* or meal-berry. The Danish name is *akselrøn*, and the Norwegian *asal*. This tree's range extends across Europe to the south of Scandinavia. The Latin specific name, *aria*, is drawn from a Roman tree.

The Swedish whitebeam is so called because it is commoner than other whitebeams in southern Sweden, but it grows in neighbouring lands and I have found it truly wild in northern Scotland, near the Moray Firth. Its Latin name, *Sorbus intermedia*, reveals the intermediate character of its leaves, midway between Common whitebeam and rowan. They are not compound, but pinnately lobed, and each lobe is toothed like a rowan leaf. The Swedish whitebeam is often grown as an ornamental tree, being hardy and smoke tolerant; it even thrives in the heart of Glasgow.

Cornish whitebeam has the Latin name *S. latifolia*, meaning broad-leaved, and can be regarded as intermediate between the Common whitebeam and the Wild service. Its leaf is broadly oval to oblong, with about three shallow lobes on each side, and a toothed edge. It forms a larger tree than any other whitebeam—suggesting hybrid vigour—and is occasionally planted for ornament. It may reach seventy-five feet high by eleven feet round. The bark is blue-grey with horizontal bands of prominent pores. The French call it *alisier de Fontainebleau*, and an old Devon name for the berries, which are edible, is 'French hales', possibly linked to *alisier*. The natural range of this tree includes south-east Ireland, Cornwall, Devon and parts of France.

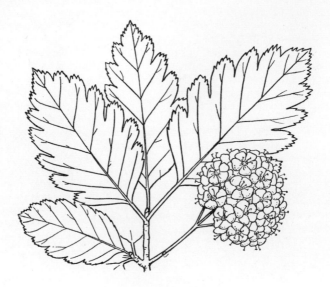

**Swedish Whitebeam**
Lobed leaves, and a flower cluster

# Medlar and Quince

*Mespilus germanica*                    ROSACEAE
and *Cydonia oblonga*

The medlar is occasionally seen as an escape from cultivation in hedgerows in the south of England, and in this wild form it bears spines which are not seen on the orchard race. It

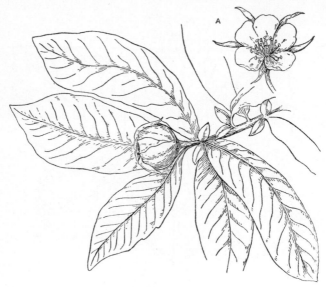

**Medlar in fruit**
A, flower

forms a much-branched small tree up to thirty feet high and two feet round, with a rough grey bark. Its leaves have a remarkable ovoid shape, being three times as long as broad, but expanding towards the end, then narrowing suddenly to a blunt tip. They are downy and almost stalkless, and each has a pair of leafy green stipules at its base. They are set alternately on the twigs. The winter twigs are hairy, and the curious lip-like projection of the leaf-scar below each many-scaled, sharp pointed brown bud aids recognition. The flowers are easily known by their five very long downy green sepals which project in the gaps between the five white petals. There are many stamens and a five-celled pistil set on a yellow downy disc where the nectar appears.

The fruit is formed by the swelling of the base of the flower, and the five sepals remain at the tip, becoming reflexed as it grows. Within the opening left between the expanded sepals, it is possible to see the hard brown papery covering of the seed chambers. The outer surface of the fruit is downy. This fruit is at first green, but becomes yellowish-brown as it ripens in late October. Until then it is sour and hard, but it suddenly becomes soft, and sweet enough to eat or to make into jelly. Then it begins to decay, attracting birds and beasts which peck or nibble its pulp and spread its hard flat seeds which have a rough, ridged surface. The fruit has little commercial value, but its piquant flavour, and the pretty form and flower of the tree, favour its cultivation.

The medlar is native to south-east Europe. *Mespilus* was its Roman name, and the possible source of our word 'medlar'; *germanica* implies that it was grown in Germany. The Germans call it *Mispel* and the French *neflier*. Medlars have been grown in England since 1500 A.D., and possibly earlier.

A tree sometimes mistaken for the medlar is the quince, *Cydonia oblonga*. This is a branchy small tree grown in orchards and occasionally seen as an escape. It has a grey bark but is spineless. Its ovoid leaves have a short stalk and a shorter and more rounded blade than those of a medlar. The long sepals are bent back from the flower, and the petals are usually tinged with pink. The fruit is broadly pear-shaped but has an irregular form. Its most distinctive features are a very strong pungent scent and a sharp flavour which is too strong-tasting for eating raw, but the pulp is used for jelly. It is yellow in colour and downy, and holds many small black ridged seeds.

The quince is native to south-east Europe and has been cultivated for centuries, being well known in England since 1611. *Cydonia* is its Greek name; *oblonga* refers to the oddly shaped fruit. Selected quince stocks, increased by means of root suckers, are widely used for grafting apples. The German name is *Quitt*. The French call the tree *cognassier* and the fruit *coing*.

## Hawthorns

*Crataegus* species                                    ROSACEAE

The hawthorns, though small trees, are of great importance in the lowland farming economy in Britain. When the old open-field system of agriculture was abandoned, permanent field boundaries were needed to replace the temporary barriers of hurdles or the herdsmen who had kept the livestock away from cropped fields. Wire had not yet been developed, so in all districts where walling stone was scarce the farmers planted miles of hawthorn hedges. These were protected by hurdles in youth, and later they were cut and laid with great skill to form living barriers of interwoven upright and slanting stems. The word 'quick', often used for hawthorn, means 'living' and reminds us that these 'live hedges' replaced the temporary 'dead hedges' of previous days. A well-tended hedge is almost everlasting, for new branches constantly spring up from small dormant buds, or from long-lived rootstocks.

The feature that caused hawthorn to be chosen for this purpose is of course its thorn, a modified short shoot ending in a sharp spine. It is dull crimson and this enables you to tell a hawthorn bush at any time of year for all other spiny bushes have thorns of other colours. The buds are very small and reddish-black with many scales (p. 49), and are set alternately on zig-zag twigs which are dull red above but green below.

The leaves are small, short-stalked, dull green and divided into many irregular lobes along each side. The bark becomes rough on old stems, breaking up into squarish plates (Plate 51); it is purplish-brown in colour. If left uncut, hawthorn forms a small tree with a rounded crown (Plate 50), up to forty feet

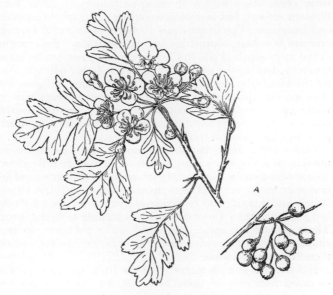

**Hawthorn in blossom**
A, fruit (haws)

high and four feet round. The wood has a white sapwood and a rust-brown heart; it is tough, and is sometimes used for mallet heads, tool handles, fence stakes, or firewood, but it is too small and irregular for most jobs.

Hawthorns burst into blossom in May and are therefore called May trees. In the common wild strain the flowers, which are borne in countless clusters on twice-branched stalks, are single and white. Decorative garden hawthorns have red or pink blossoms and may be double; such kinds are grafted on the common stock. Each normal flower has five sepals, five petals, many anthers and a pistil with from one to three cells. Many people think it is unlucky to bring May blossom indoors, but everyone enjoys its gay display in garden and hedgerow. The fruits ripen in October as round berries, crimson in colour, topped by five woody scales—the remains of the calyx sepals (Plate 61). They are sour, but can be made into jelly. During the winter the berries are gradually stripped by the birds who digest their acid, mealy pulp and pass out their stones. Hence young hawthorns spring up everywhere on waste land which they colonize vigorously. Eventually the hawthorn scrub is replaced by taller trees, such as oaks which grow up under the protection of its spines.

Under cultivation, hawthorn berries must be stored in moist sand for eighteen months before their seeds will sprout. The seedling raises two oval, blunt-ended seed-leaves, and its first true leaves are oval with toothed edges, but not lobed. Its growth is rapid, and two-year-old plants are used for new hedges, being then a foot high and beginning to bear thorns. These protect the leaves which are quite palatable; in fact children nibble the newly opened emerald green ones, calling them 'bread-and-cheese'.

Hawthorn draws its name from its fruit, the haw; it was so-called hundreds of years before it was used for hedges. Dutch *hagedoorn*, German *Hagedorn*, and Norwegian and Swedish *hagtorn* are allied names. It is also called whitethorn, but only in contrast to the blackthorn (p. 84) for its thorns are really reddish-brown, though its bark is pale grey; *hvidtjørn*, the Danish name, is linked to this.

Other names meaning 'white thorn' are: Welsh *draenen wen;* Gaelic *sgitheach geal*; and Irish *sgeaċ geal*. Other Celtic names are Welsh *ysbydadden* and Gaelic *droigheann*, meaning thorn. The French *aubépine* also means 'white thorn'.

*Crataegus* is in origin the Greek name of a tree, not well identified. The genus has two species native to Britain. The Common hawthorn, *C. monogyna*, has a single stigma and only one stone in the berry, implied by its Latin name of 'one female'. It grows throughout the British Isles. The Midland hawthorn, *C. oxyacanthoides*, has two or three stigmas and also two or three stones in each berry. Its leaves are broader, with fewer lobes than the common sort, and the flowers are somewhat bell-shaped. The Midland hawthorn is found only in the midlands, the south and the east of England and neighbouring Welsh counties. It is seen more often as a tree of damp woodlands than as a hedge shrub. *Oxyacanthoides* means 'white-thorn-like'.

# Dogwood

*Cornus sanguinea*                                    CORNACEAE

Abandoned pastures on the chalk downs are quickly invaded by this singular small tree or shrub, which can be known at once by its blood-red twigs and opposite, simple leaves with curved veins. It is common on all lime-rich soils, though scarce elsewhere; its natural range includes Britain as far north as the Forth, Ireland and the south-west of Norway and Sweden, all Denmark and the rest of central and southern Europe. In winter the slender naked grey buds (p. 40) are distinctive, and in autumn the leaves assume the same deep red shade as the twigs. The lower bark is greenish-grey, but the stem is never more than a foot round.

In June the dogwood opens clusters of pretty white flowers (Plate 53) which spring from the axils of the leaves but stand well above them. Each has four tiny sepals, four petals, four stamens, and a two-celled pistil. They attract bees by their nectar and a faint, pleasant scent. By autumn they have ripened to glossy black berries, each holding a single hard seed, which are very decorative (Plate 66). The seeds are spread by birds who swallow the pulpy berry and void the hard stone. This explains why thickets of dogwood scrub, almost impenetrable to man, spring up so quickly on waste land, but the bushes also spread by sucker shoots. Eventually they are replaced by woods of taller, longer-lived trees, such as oak. If the seed is stored in moist sand it germinates eighteen months after ripening, sending up two oval seed-leaves.

The branches of dogwood hold a hard strong white wood, which makes good skewers. This feature explains its name, for a 'dog' (a term still used by timber-men) is a sharp spike; another name is gad-tree or goad tree, from the goads once used to prod oxen pulling ploughs. *Cornus* in Latin, *crann coirnel* in Irish, and *cornouiller* in French mean 'horny' in allusion to the texture of the wood; *sanguinea*, bloody, refers to the colour of the twigs. In German this tree is *Hornstrauch*, horny-wooded shrub, and in Danish *rød kornel*, a name derived from the Latin. Elsewhere in Scandinavia it is called *hornved*, horny-wood. In Ireland the dogwood is called *crann mucosa* and in Wales it is *cwyrosen*, or wax tree, because the berries yield an oil. Also called *Thelycrania sanguinea*.

Here and there on hill tops from the Cheviots northwards you may find the related rare Dwarf cornel, *Cornus suecica*. This is a low shrubby perennial, under one foot high, which bears white flowers in June, followed by dark red berries on four-sided stems, in autumn. A relic of the ancient arctic-alpine vegetation, it is found at much lower levels in Norway, where it is called *skrubbaer*. Recently it has been placed in a new genus with the name *Chamaepericlymenum suecicum*.

## Elder

*Sambucus nigra*                              CAPRIFOLIACEAE

Most people know the elder by its remarkable twigs, which are stout but brittle, since they hold the thickest pith of any tree. Children hollow them out to make pea-shooters, pop guns, or musical pipes, and many of the tree's names recall these hollowed stems. The Latin name *sambucus* is linked with

Greek *sambuke*, a music-pipe, while *nigra*, black, refers to the berries. In German it is *Schwarzer Holunder*, from the verb *hohlen*, to hollow out. In Scotland it is known as the bore-tree, since it has a bore or tubular hollow like a gun. The Welsh name, *ysgawen*, comes from the root *cau*, meaning hollow.

**Elder**
A, berries; B, portion of flower-cluster

In Scandinavia it is called *hyll*, related to *hul*, a hole, and our own name of elder began as Anglo-Saxon *ellearn*, again linked to the idea of hollowing out. Other names are the French *sureau* and the Gaelic and Irish *ruis, trom, truim* or *druman.*

As further clues to its identity, the twigs are often angular and bear corky pores vertically disposed on their grey-brown bark. The pith is used by botanists in the laboratory to support leaves and other soft tissues so that they can be cut with a razor to yield specimens for the microscope. Jewellers use it, too, for cleaning watch mechanisms. Elder pith is one of the lightest-known substances, holding much air and little true tissue. As the stems age the pith slowly breaks up, and at the heart of the stoutest elder trunk you can find the large pith-tube it leaves. The wood of the trunk and large branches is very hard and white, and horny in texture. It is used occasion-ally for turnery and carving, and is also cut into fine wooden pins for laboratory work and watchmaker's probes. The bark rapidly becomes furrowed and corky. It is thick and greyish-brown in colour.

Elder buds are oppositely set, with a clear leaf scar below them and several loose brownish-red or even purple scales (p. 42). They turn green early and in a mild winter they may start growth in January, though hard frosts cut them back. The leaves are pinnately compound with toothed edges and resemble those of the ash, which are also oppositely placed; but the elder leaf has fewer leaflets, commonly five to seven, while the ash has at least nine (p. 25). Cultivated varieties include Golden elder, var. *aurea*, with yellow leaves, and Parsley-leaved elder, var. *laciniata*, with much-divided ones. The leaves and all green tissues hold a glucoside related to prussic acid, and are distasteful to livestock. They were once made into Green Elder ointment to treat sprains and bruises.

In June the fragrant white flowers of the elder open in large loose clusters above the foliage (Plate 52). Each blossom has five sepals, five petals united at the base, five stamens and a pistil with three cells. Elder-flower water was once used to flavour cakes and wines, or to add scent to cosmetics. Pollina-tion is done mainly by insects, but a good deal of the pollen is airborne.

The lustrous purplish-black berries, which ripen in late

September, can be eaten raw but they have an insipid taste. Country people still bake them in pies, or ferment them, with the help of a good deal of sugar, into elderberry wine; if dried they can be used like currants. The birds, especially starlings, gather most of them and later void the small hard black seeds; this enables elder to spring up everywhere on waste ground or along hedgerows where birds roost. Gathered seed, kept in moist sand, sprouts the spring after ripening. The seedling bears two small oval seed-leaves on a long slender stalk; simple leaves with toothed edges follow; then leaves with three leaflets; the normal compound form is developed later. Cuttings take root very readily.

Elder grows wild everywhere in Britain and Ireland, and even in the Outer Hebrides. It is native to most of Europe and is cultivated in America. Though often a mere bush, it can form a tree forty feet high and seven feet round. It thrives best on soils rich in nitrogen, and therefore grows well close to farmyards, in rabbit warrens and beside badger setts. Rabbits find it unpalatable, though they eat every other tree. Badgers use its soft bark to clean their claws by scratching; and the height of the scratches shows the size of the badger. Elder thrives in smoky cities and also grows on sea cliffs, though salt scorches its leaves. Sometimes its twigs bear the curious purple fructifications of the Jew's Ear fungus, which are shaped like a human ear; this may explain the widely-held belief that Judas Iscariot hanged himself from an elder tree. Elder leaves yield a green dye, its bark a black one, and its berries blues, lilacs and violets, also a black hair dye.

In Scottish woods, and locally in England and Wales you may find the Red-berried elder, *Sambucus racemosa*, a shrub with more deeply toothed leaves, greenish flowers and scarlet berries. This is generally held to have been introduced to provide food and cover for pheasants, but its seeds could have been brought over from Scandinavia by migratory birds. It is now fully naturalized and native birds help to spread it.

# Wayfaring Tree

*Viburnum lantana*                    CAPRIFOLIACEAE

The poetic name of this charming tree was given to it by the herbalist Gerard in 1597, because he saw it so often in his journeys over the downs between Wiltshire and London. Of all our trees it is the one most strikingly attached to chalk and limestone; on such soils it can be found as far north as Yorkshire, but it is only common in the south. Its natural range includes western, central and southern Europe, but it is not found in Ireland nor in Scandinavia. It was the *viburnum* of the Romans, a word which gives *viorne* (*cotonneuse*) in French, though the usual French name is *mancienne;* the specific name *lantana* records a resemblance to a tropical shrub. Its original English name was 'hoarwithy' and there is a village of this name where it grows in Herefordshire. The 'hoar' refers to its hoary leaves, white with downy hairs, and the 'withy' to its twigs which are as pliant as those of a willow. In Germany it is called *Wolliger Schneeball*, woolly snowball-tree, because of its downy leaves and round clusters of white flowers.

In winter you will know the Wayfaring tree at once by its odd twigs and buds. The twigs are brown, but covered with white hairs. The buds, in opposite pairs, have no outer scales, so you can see the details of the unfolded leaves already exposed; larger buds at the branch tips, also 'naked', show the structure of the future flower cluster (p. 40). In summer the opposite, oval, woolly leaves, with prominent veins and toothed edges, make the tree easily recognizable. The flowers open in June, and though individually small, form showy clusters (Plate 54); each has five sepals, five white petals, five stamens, and a two- or three-celled pistil. In autumn, when its leaves turn to crimson, the wayfaring tree attracts our attention by its gay, many-hued fruits; they ripen from green through white and red to black, and three colours appear together in one cluster (Plate 71). They tempt people to pick them for indoor decoration, but they prove disappointing for they have a strong, sickly-sweet smell, and soon rot into pulp. Each holds a single hard seed which germinates eighteen months after ripening, sending up a slender stalk topped by two oval seed-leaves.

Birds are very fond of Wayfaring tree berries and spread the tree freely along hedgerows and over waste ground everywhere on the chalk downs. The woolly covering on the twigs, buds and lower surface of the leaves restricts the transpiration of water and enables the tree to thrive in the very driest of places, even where no soil covers the chalk. The twigs, though very thin, are exceptionally tough and pliant, and it takes a real effort to break them; they have long been used by shepherds and foresters on the downs to tie up bundles, just like string. Older branches are brittle and have a remarkably thick pale brown pith. The bark becomes pinkish-grey and fibrous on stout stems. The wood is pale creamy brown, with a slight odour; it has sometimes been used in turnery. A wayfaring tree can grow to fifteen feet, but is often only a straggling bush.

# Guelder Rose

*Viburnum opulus*                                    CAPRIFOLIACEAE

In autumn the scarlet berries of the wild guelder rose are a lovely sight. They stand out in upright clusters, reflecting the sunlight from both their smooth outer skin and their inner, translucent flesh. Beside them stand leaves that turn from dull green to rust red or scarlet (Plate 72). The twigs are reddish-brown also, and somewhat angular, while at the base of each leaf-stalk there are two reddish stipules. The guelder rose is easily known in winter by its oppositely set, greenish-yellow buds on ridged twigs with a very small terminal bud (p. 41). In summer you can pick it out by leaves that are both opposite and divided into lobes, three or five in number. The leaves of sycamore and maples are similar, but guelder rose has only three main veins at the base. There are also two glands at the base of each leaf-blade.

The white, attractive flowers of the guelder rose are quite peculiar and account for its odd name. They open in June in

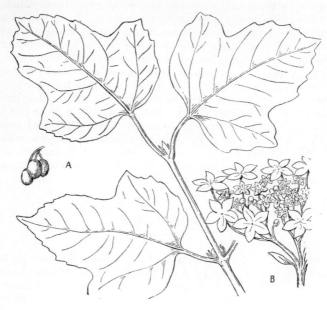

**Guelder Rose**
A, fruit; B, flowers

branched clusters, and each cluster holds two types of flower. The outer ones bear five sepals and five creamy-white petals, but are wholly sterile, lacking both stamens and pistil. Their purpose is to attract insects to the inner flowers, which are green and inconspicuous but hold five stamens and a pistil with two or three cells, and nectaries to reward the insects. Each fertile flower yields a single hard seed within the red pulp. About 400 years ago a peculiar form of this wild tree, namely the variety *sterilis*, was noticed in Guelderland (Gelderland) a district of Holland. This race or 'sport' had all its flowers sterile and each flower-head was thus very showy, but it could not set seeds. Ingenious gardeners therefore propagated it by layering—bending down branches into the earth so that they took root—and it has been increased in this way ever since. The rounded heads of white flowers at once suggest a snowball so the common name for the Guelder rose is 'snowball tree'. It is not even distantly linked to the true rose.

In Germany this tree is called, even in its wild form, *Schneeball*, and 'snowball' may be its original English name. In France it is known as *obier* or *viorne obier*. The Danes call it *kvalkved*, a word that was originally *kvalkenbærtræ*, literally 'qualm-berry-tree' because the acid fruits cause stomach-ache. In Norway it is called *korsved*, crosswood, from the opposite twigs. The *opulus* of the Latin is an unidentified tree. In America the wild guelder rose is called 'European cranberry bush', but it is not a cranberry. The Welsh name is *corswigen*, meaning 'marsh bush'.

There are many conflicting statements about guelder rose berries; they are said to poison people, also wolves, but are supposed to be good to eat if mixed with honey and flour! Certainly they are sour and contain valerianic acid, and the birds leave them alone until late winter. Eventually the birds *do* eat them, however, and spread the seeds to damp woodlands throughout Britain and Ireland and over most of Europe. Gathered seed does not sprout until eighteen months after falling. It should be stored in moist sand. The oval seed-leaves expand on a long stalk, above ground. Bushes also spread by sucker shoots. The greatest height recorded is sixteen feet.

# Strawberry Tree

*Arbutus unedo*                                    ERICACEAE

In a few places in the west of Ireland this fascinating tree grows truly wild. Its main centre lies in the south-west, in County Kerry, around the Lakes of Killarney. It is also found in the south-west of County Cork and beside Lough Gill in County Sligo, well to the north. Otherwise you must go to Brittany, Spain and Portugal and the Mediterranean shores to see it growing naturally, for it is one of our 'Lusitanian' plants, members of the flora of south-west Europe that have somehow come to our westerly shores. It is an evergreen adapted to thrive in a wet winter and to restrict its transpiration through a dry summer. Its leaves are leathery, oval and pointed, with toothed edges and a prominent mid-rib. They are dark green and smooth above, paler below, and are borne alternately on short reddish stalks, which carry glandular hairs. The buds are small, sharply pointed and crimson, as are the young shoots.

The Strawberry tree flowers from September to January, bearing bunches of small white flowers near the tips of its twigs; these flowers are scentless but bear nectar to attract insects. The oval, reddish buds open their five sepals to expose a white waxy bell, rather like that of the lily-of-the-valley, and composed of five united petals within which stand ten stamens and a five-celled pistil. The fruit takes a whole year to ripen, so both flower and fruit can be seen on the tree at one time. At first it is a small green globe, but it swells into a strawberry-red structure with a knobbly surface, looking very like a garden strawberry. The seeds, however, lie at the centre, not on the surface; they are small and brown, and are spread by birds that eat the fruit. The yellow pulp has a mealy texture and an insipid taste. Pliny invented the specific name *unedo*, literally 'one I eat', to show they were unattractive; yet they are quite wholesome and were eaten by the Irish in past times of scarcity.

The flower, foliage and general bushy form of the Strawberry tree shows its relation to the heaths, and it is placed in
the same botanical family. As a rule it is a much-branched,
small tree (Plate 55) but it can reach a height of thirty feet and
a girth of nine feet. The bark is rusty-brown and eventually

**Strawberry Tree**
bearing flowers and fruit together

breaks away in strips. The trunk has a yellow sapwood and a
dark red-brown heartwood. It is suitable for turnery and
carving, and what little is harvested in Ireland is used to make
souvenirs for visitors. The seed germinates in the spring after

ripening. Seedlings, often found in the Killarney woods, have two deep green seed-leaves with reddish rims, enclosed at first in the seed coat; shiny green early leaves, fringed with long hairs, follow.

The Strawberry tree is often grown in gardens. It needs a lime-free soil and grows best in the milder climates of the south and west for the seedlings are tender and cannot stand hard frosts.

There are two Irish names for this tree: *suglair*, and *cuinche* or *caithne*, which is pronounced 'cahny'. It occurs in place-names where the tree is not now found, indicating a wider spread in the past. *Arbutus* is the original Latin name. The French call it *l'arbousier*, and the Germans *Erdbeerbaum*.

## Ash

*Fraxinus excelsior*                                    OLEACEAE

Ash can be told at once by its leaf which is compounded of many leaflets set along a grooved mid-rib or petiole; it has a long stalk and ends in a single terminal leaflet; each separate leaflet is oval, ends in a point, and has a shallowly toothed edge. The leaves are always borne in opposite pairs and are bigger than those of any tree with a similar foliage plan. There are commonly from seven to fifteen leaflets, and the whole leaf may be a foot long. In winter the buds are equally well-marked; all of them, except for terminal buds, are set in opposite pairs and have a rough jet-black surface. The smooth greenish-grey twigs that bear them are usually flattened at each pair of buds (p. 41). Knobbly short shoots that do not grow longer are also found. The opposite branching pattern leads to a remarkably open crown built up in an angular fashion and best seen in winter (Plate 57). But if a terminal bud is damaged, two side buds try to take the lead together, and a forked stem, of less value to the timber merchant, results.

Ash bursts into leaf later than any other tree, never before the end of April. During its brief summer spell of activity the preading crown of pale green leaves is a glorious sight (Plate 56), but the leaves turn yellow and fall early in October. They come down in one piece, and attract earthworms, who drag the blades down into their burrows and leave the stalks in view, standing out at odd angles. Goats and sheep enjoy green ash foliage, and young trees cannot survive if exposed to

**Ash leaf and fruits** (keys)

grazing. The bark, smooth at first, soon becomes broken up by a regular network of ribs and hollows; it is a soft fawnish-grey (ash-grey) in colour (Plate 58).

Ash flowers are simple, wind-pollinated structures which appear just as the leaves do. Usually they are hidden by foliage, but in a cold spring when leafing is late they stand out as purplish-green tassels on the bare twigs (Plate 60). They may be male, female or have organs of both sexes, and the same tree may bear flowers of all three kinds. They spring from the twig in a cluster, each on its short stalk, and have no sepals or petals. A 'complete' flower has two stamens with purple anthers, set on either side of a one-celled pistil. A male flower has no pistil, while a female flower lacks stamens.

After pollination the pistils develop into slender green structures, each holding a single seed and ending in a wing. If they are plucked while ripe, but still green, the seeds will sprout the same summer. Normally they hang on the trees far into the winter, as conspicuous festoons of winged brown seeds. These are called 'keys' because they are shaped like the keys used for ancient locks. The winter gales gradually blow them away over distances up to hundreds of yards. They then lie dormant in the soil for fifteen months or so, and the forester who gathers brown ash seed for sowing has to store them in moist sand for a like period. Ash seedlings, which spring up freely in gardens anywhere near an ash tree, have at first two long oval seed-leaves. The next pair of leaves is simple and oval, and the pair after that has only three leaflets. The compound pattern of the adult tree then follows.

A weeping form of ash, var. *pendula*, is grown in gardens by grafting on a common ash stock, but it always needs training.

The wood of ash is easily recognized. It is a uniform pale brown in colour, sometimes with a darker heart, but its surface is crossed at intervals by clear bands or rings of open pores. These are the vessels of the springwood, which carry the first rush of spring sap; the summerwood, formed later, is hard, dense and strong. Users of ash prefer fast-grown wood, because it has relatively more summerwood, and merchants pay good prices for trees grown quickly on rich soils. The exacting uses for which tough ash timber is prized include: tool handles of all kinds, especially those for hammers, axes and picks, which must withstand repeated shocks; sports goods, including

billiard cues, tennis rackets, hockey sticks and oars, for like
reasons; cart shafts, rims of wooden wheels and the framing
of motor vehicles—again where shock-proof timber is needed.
For some of these purposes cleft ash is preferred to sawn timber,
because its grain is never broken. In the past ash was used for
weapons, especially the shafts of spears and lances.

Ash is also an attractive furniture wood. Some is used for
cleft bar hurdles, but it will not serve for permanent fencing,
unless creosoted, because it has no natural durability out of
doors. Because of its high content of true wood substance it is
a first-class firewood and will burn even when green.

Ash arrived in Britain about 6000 B.C., and is now found
wild right to the far north of Scotland, and also in Ireland and
the Outer Hebrides. It thrives particularly well on limestone,
and several natural woods survive on such rocks, often amid
crags, with trees rooting in clefts where the sheep cannot
destroy seedlings. Foresters prefer to plant it on deep rich
soils where quick growth ensures high-priced timber. If a
young tree is cut back it sends up coppice shoots with great
vigour; these make tough walking-sticks. Ash must always have
full sunlight, but it resists exposure well and thrives 1,450 feet
above sea level in Breconshire. Ash is found right across
northern Europe, high up the Alps and in southern Norway,
Sweden and Finland. The ash Yggdrasil, famous in Norse
mythology, sent its branches up to heaven, its roots down to
hell!

*Fraxinus* was the Roman name of ash, and is the source of
the French *frêne*. The specific name *excelsior*, meaning higher,
is well chosen; an ash at Duncombe Park near Helmsley in
Yorkshire reaches 148 feet and is our second tallest broadleaved tree. But ash does not live remarkably long, nor grow
very stout; the greatest girth recorded, at Holywell Hall,
Lincolnshire, is only nineteen and a half feet. Our name
'ash' comes, from Anglo-Saxon *aesc*, allied to German *Esche*
and Dutch *esch;* but also in part from *ask*, the Scandinavian
name. Askrigg, meaning ash ridge, in Yorkshire is an example

of ash in a Norse place-name; Ashurst, ash clump, in Hampshire dates from still earlier Jutish settlement. The Welsh
name, *onnen*, has two collective forms, *onn* and *ynn*; it is
related to Gaelic *uinseann* and Irish *fuinseog*.

# Lilac

*Syringa vulgaris*                                    OLEACEAE

The lilac branches so often that its form becomes more bushy
than tree-like (Plate 62); but it often reaches tree height, up to
twenty feet or so, and develops a truly woody stem. In winter
its twigs are easily recognized by its green opposite buds, and
the fact that nearly every twig ends with *two* buds, not three
as in other opposite-budded trees (p. 41). In effect a terminal
bud is rarely formed, so two side buds take over its work and
the twigs branch repeatedly. In summer the smooth heart-
shaped leaves, set in pairs and mid-green in colour, are
distinctive. The showy flowers, which open in June, are borne
in spikes or panicles, with the youngest at the tip. The spike
has a long stalk, with flowers rising directly from it. Each
flower has four sepals united to form a tube, four pale
purple petals also forming a tube, two stamens and a two-
celled pistil. Pollination is by insects, and in autumn each
flower ripens a grey hard capsule, with two chambers each
holding two small hard narrow seeds. These seeds have a
wrinkled surface and are brown in colour with a narrow paler
papery wing all round them. They are spread by the wind and
sprout next spring; yet in Britain lilac rarely becomes naturalized in this way. In hedges and old gardens its renews itself
by fresh shoots from the rootstock.

The bark of lilac is grey and fibrous, forming long strands
on stout trunks. The wood is very hard, smooth and dead white
on the outside, but the heartwood is tinged, surprisingly, with
the lilac colour of the flower. It is sometimes used for
decorative woodwork. It burns well.

Lilac is native to Persia, and its common name comes from

*lilas*, Persian for blue. It is applied, of course, to the colour of the flowers of the common race; white and dark purple strains are also grown, being increased by layering or root cuttings. *Syringa*, the Latin name, comes from Greek *syrinx*,

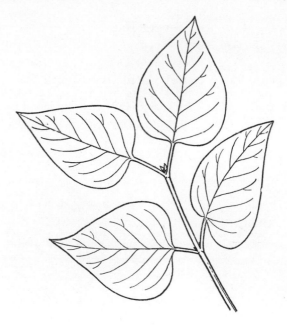

**Lilac**
Paired terminal buds and opposite, heart-shaped leaves

a reed, because the pith is easily removed from thin branches to leave a hollow tube which can be shaped into a pipe or flute; *vulgaris* means common. One German name, *Holunder*, implies the same hollow-stem idea; another German name is

*Flieder*. In Denmark the lilac is called *syren*, in Wales *lelogen* and in France *lilas*. Lilac was introduced from the East in the sixteenth century, and has now become naturalized in many European lands.

## Sweet Bay

*Laurus nobilis*                                             LAURACEAE

The Sweet bay is a beautiful evergreen tree with lustrous dark green leaves carried on reddish-coloured stalks, set alternately along the twigs (Plate 63). It can be told from similar trees, and in particular from the cherry laurel (p. 98), by the strong aroma that is evident as soon as these leaves are

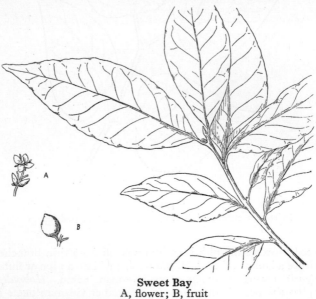

**Sweet Bay**
A, flower; B, fruit

Pl. 2

**Tulip Tree** (p. 54)

Pl. 3

Flowers of Lime (p. 57)

Pl. 4    **Leaves, bracts and fruits of Lime** (p. 57)

Pl. 5

**A Lime tree in Kew Gardens, summer**  (p. 56)

Pl. 6

**Lime tree in winter** (p. 56)

Pl. 7

**Bole of Lime tree** (p. 58)

Pl. 8

**Holly trees** (p. 60)

Flowers and leaves of Holly (p. 60)

Pl. 9

Pl. 10

**Spindle Tree** (p. 63)

Pl. 11

**Holly berries** (p. 61)

Pl. 12

**Alder Buckthorn** (p. 67)

Pl. 13

Horse Chestnut in bloom, summer (p. 70)

Pl. 14

**Spindle leaves and berries, autumn** (p. 64)

Pl. 15

Horse Chestnut in winter (p. 70)

Pl. 16

**Bole of Horse Chestnut** (p. 70)

Pl. 17
**Leaves, thorns and berries of Purging Buckthorn** (p. 65)

Pl. 18
**Berries and foliage of Alder Buckthorn, autumn** (p. 67)

Pl. 19

**Field Maple tree** (p. 75)

Pl. 20

**Sycamore tree** (p. 72)

Pl. 21
**Fruits, leaves and buds of Horse Chestnut** (p. 70)

Pl. 22

**Sycamore in winter** (p. 72)

Pl. 23

**Bole of Sycamore** (p. 73)

Sycamore flowers (p. 73)

Pl. 24

Pl. 25

**Flowers of Norway maple** (p. 76)

Pl. 26          **Laburnum tree in blossom** (p. 79)

Pl. 27

**Locust tree** (p. 83)

Pl. 28

**Bole of Locust tree** (p. 83)

Pl. 29

**A clump of Blackthorn** (p. 85)

Pl. 30

**Flowers of Wild Plum** (p. 87)

Pl. 31

**Gean tree in bloom** (p. 89)

Pl. 32

**Flowers and leaves of Horse Chestnut** (p. 70)

Pl. 33

**Bole of Gean** (p. 89)

Flowers and foliage of Gean (p. 91)

Pl. 34

Pl. 35

**Fruits and leaves of Sycamore** (p. 74)

Pl. 36

Copper-leaved Plum (p. 89)

Pl. 37

**Japanese Cherry** (p. 94)

**Bird Cherry** (p. 95)

Pl. 38

Pl. 39

**Almond** (p. 96)

Pl. 40

**Cherry Laurel** (p. 99)

Pl. 41

**Wild Pear** (p. 100)

Pl. 42

**Bole of Wild Pear** (p. 101)

Pl. 43

**Flowers and foliage of Crab Apple** (p. 103)

Pl. 44      **Crab Apples** (p. 103)

Crab Apple tree (p. 102)

Pl. 45

Pl. 46

**Bole of Crab Apple** (p. 102)

Pl. 47

**Whitebeam in blossom** (p. 110)

Pl. 48

**A windswept Rowan** (p. 105)

Pl. 49

**Rowan blossoms and foliage** (p. 105)

Pl. 50

Hawthorn tree in bloom (p. 115)

Pl. 51

**Hawthorn bole** (p. 115)

Pl. 52

**Elder** (p. 120)

Dogwood flowers (p. 117)

Pl. 53

Pl. 54

**Wayfaring Tree** (p. 122)

Pl. 55

**Strawberry Tree** (p. 127)

Pl. 56

**Ash in summer** (p: 129)

Pl. 57

**Ash in winter** (p. 128)

Pl. 58

**Bole of Ash** (p. 129)

Pl. 59

**Sloes, the fruit of the Blackthorn** (p. 86)

Pl. 60

**Ash flowers** (p. 130)

Pl. 61

**Haws, the fruit of the Hawthorn** (p. 116)

Pl. 62

**White Lilac** (p. 132)

Sweet Bay tree (p 134)

Pl. 63

Pl. 64

**Tree of Heaven** (p. 135)

Pl. 65

**Box trees** (p. 139)

Pl. 66

**Dogwood leaves and berries** (p. 117)

Pl. 67

**Wych Elm in summer** (p. 143)

Pl. 68

**Wych Elm in winter** (p. 143)

Pl. 69

**Bole of Wych Elm** (p. 143)

Pl. 70

**English Elm in summer** (p. 144)

Pl. 71

**Leaves and berries of Wayfaring Tree** (p. 122)

Pl. 72

**Guelder Rose leaves and berries** (p. 123)

Pl. 73

**English Elm in winter** (p. 144)

Pl. 74

**Bole of English Elm** (p. 144)

Pl. 75

**Mulberry Tree** (p. 148)

Pl. 76

Leaves and fruits of Mulberry (p. 148)

Pl. 77

**Plane tree in summer** (p. 151)

Pl. 78

Plane tree in winter (p. 151)

Pl. 79

**Bole of Plane** (p. 149)

Walnut (p. 152)

Pl. 80

Pl. 81

**Bole of Walnut** (p. 152)

Pl. 82

Birch in summer (p. 155)

Pl. 83

**Birch trees in winter** (p. 155)

Pl. 84

**Birch bole** (p. 155)

Pl. 85
**Birch catkins—female above, male below** (p. 156)

Pl. 86

**Alder trees** (p. 160)

Pl. 87

**Hornbeam** (p. 166)

Pl. 88

**Hornbeam bole** (p. 164)

Pl. 89

**Hazel** (p. 167)

Hazel catkins (p. 168)

Pl. 90

Pl. 91

**Bole of Oak** (p. 171)

Pl. 92

**Fruits, seed, leaves and twigs of Walnut** (p. 153)

An open-grown Pedunculate Oak in summer (p. 171)

Pl. 93

Pl. 94

**A forest-grown Sessile Oak in winter** (p. 171)

Pl. 95

**Holm Oak** (p. 175)

Pl. 96       **Sweet Chestnut in summer** (p. 179)

Pl. 97

**Sweet Chestnut in winter** (p 179)

Pl. 98    Sweet Chestnut foliage and flowers—male above, female below (p. 177)

Pl. 99

**Bole of Sweet Chestnut** (p. 179)

Pl. 100

An open-grown Beech in summer (p. 184)

Pl. 101
**Kingscote Beechwood, Gloucestershire, in winter** (p. 184)

Pl. 102

Foliage and fruits of Beech (p. 182)

Pl. 103
**Alder in spring: cones and male catkins above,
female catkins below** (p. 160)

Pl. 104

**Bole of Beech** (p. 184)

Pl. 105          **White Willow** (p. 189)

Pl. 106

**Bole of Cricket Bat Willow** (p. 191)

Pl. 107

**Female catkins of Crack Willow** (p. 192)

Pl. 108

**Weeping Willow** (p. 193)

Pl. 109
**Pedunculate Oak foliage, with female flowers above (left),
male flowers below** (p. 171)

Pl. 110

**Crack Willow** (p. 192)

Almond-leaved Willow in winter (p. 194)

Pl. 111

Pl. 112

Almond-leaved Willow; Bay-leaved Willow; Goat Willow, Crack Willow; White Willow (pages 189, 191, 194, 195)

Pl. 113

**Purple Osier** (p. 200)

Pl. 114    **Acorns and autumn leaves of Oak** (p. 172)

Pl. 115

**Male catkins of Aspen** (p. 205)

Pl. 116

**White Poplar** (p. 207)

Pl. 117

**Bole of White Poplar** (p. 207)

Pl. 118

**Black Italian Poplar in summer** (p. 212)

Pl. 119

**Black Italian Poplar in winter** (p. 212)

Pl. 120

**Bole of Black Italian Poplar** (p. 212)

Pl. 121

**Opening fruits and foliage of Western Balsam Poplar** (p. 212)

Pl. 122

**Lombardy Poplars in summer** (p. 209)

Pl. 123

**Lombardy Poplar in winter** (p. 209)

Pl. 124

**Bole of Lombardy Poplar** (p. 210)

**Yew** (p. 217)

Pl. 125

Pl. 126
**Bole of the Selborne Yew, Hampshire** (p. 217)

Pl. 127

**Monkey Puzzle** (p. 221)

Pl. 128

**European Silver Fir** (p. 224)

Pl. 129

**Bole of Silver Fir** (p. 223)

Pl. 130

**Bole of Norway Spruce** (p. 231)

Pl. 131

**Noble Fir cone and foliage** (p. 225)

Pl. 132

**Douglas Fir** (p. 226)

Pl. 133
Douglas Firs, 150 feet tall and 100 years old,
at Bolderwood, New Forest (p. 227)

Pl. 134

**Western Hemlock in winter** (p. 230)

Pl. 135

Cones and foliage, under and upper sides,
of Western Hemlock (p. 228)

Pl. 136

**Norway Spruce** (p. 231)

Pl. 137

Pl. 138

**Serbian Spruce trees** (p. 233)

Pl. 139

**European Larch** (p. 235)

Pl. 140

**Bole of European Larch** (p. 234)

Cedar of Lebanon (p. 237)

Pl. 141

Pl. 142

**Bole of Cedar of Lebanon** (p. 236)

Scots Pine: foliage, male flowers on left, female flowers on right, and a one-year old cone (p. 240)

Pl. 143

Pl. 144

**Bole of Scots Pine** (p. 240)

Pl. 145

**Mountain Pines** (p. 243)

Pl. 146
**Cones and foliage of Lodgepole Pine** (p. 243)

Pl. 147

**Austrian Pine** (p. 243)

Pl. 148

**Corsican Pine** (p. 243)

Pl. 149

**Bole of Corsican Pine** (p. 243)

Pl. 150

**Maritime Pine** (p. 244)

Pl. 151

**Stone Pine** (p. 245)

Pl. 152

Monterey Pine (p. 245)

Pl. 153

**Yew leaves and berries** (p. 217)

Pl. 154

**Corsican Pine needles and cones** (p. 243)

Pl. 155

**Cembran Pine** (p. 246)

Pl. 156

**Weymouth Pine cone** (p. 246)

Pl. 157

**Californian Redwood**  (p. 248)

Pl. 158

**Wellingtonias** (p. 250)

Pl. 159

**Wellingtonia cones and foliage** (p. 249)

Pl. 160

**Swamp Cypress** (p. 250)

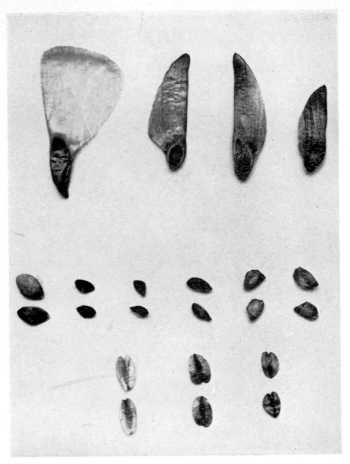

Pl. 161

**Conifer seeds.**
Top row: **Noble Fir, Scots Pine, Corsican Pine, Weymouth Pine**
Centre: **Seeds of pines, spruces and larches, after removal of wings**
Bottom: **Western Red Cedar, Wellingtonia, and Californian Redwood**
(pages 224, 241, 243, 246, 248, 249, 255)

Pl. 162

**A young Dawn Cypress** (p. 252)

Pl. 163     Japanese Cedar foliage, with young and old cones (p. 253)

Pl. 164

**Western Red Cedars** (p. 255)

Pl. 165
European Larch, showing foliage, female flowers (left), male
flowers (centre) and cones (right) (p. 235)

Pl. 166
**Cones and foliage of Western Red Cedar** (p. 255)

Pl. 167

**Incense Cedar** (p. 256)

Pl. 168

**Lawson Cypress** (p. 257)

Pl. 169

**Bole of Lawson Cypress** (p. 258)

Pl. 170
**Foliage and cones of Norway Spruce** (p. 232)

Pl. 171

**Monterey Cypress** (p. 259)

Pl. 172

Juniper bush on the Wiltshire Downs (p. 260)

Pl. 173    **Juniper needles and berries** (p. 260)

Pl. 174
Foliage of Virginian Juniper (p. 263)
with juvenile needles (above, left) and adult ones (above right).
Foliage of Dawn Cypress below (p. 253)

Pl. 175

**Maidenhair Tree** (p. 263)

crushed. If a leaf is held up to the light it will be seen that its margin is white and translucent, another key feature.

The bay bears male and female flowers on separate trees; both kinds grow in small short-stalked groups, each has four sepals and four petals and they are yellowish-white in colour. Male flowers hold twelve stamens apiece. Female flowers have a single-celled pistil, and the one-seeded berries that develop from them are at first green, but ripen to a lustrous purplish-black by October. They are no good to eat, but attract the birds that spread the seeds. The bay also renews itself by suckers from its roots, which often form a thicket close to the original main stem. Its bark is black, with paler cracks on old trunks.

The Sweet bay is a native of the Mediterranean lands which has been introduced to southern England as a decorative tree. It thrives surprisingly well in tubs or large pots, so it is occasionally seen ornamenting town yards. The leaves are used to flavour cooked dishes, especially in casseroles or for soused fish, and are often included in tins of Portuguese sardines. Sweet bay is believed to be the true laurel of Greece and Rome, and its leaves were used to make wreaths for the brows of poets, athletes and conquerors. Our name 'bay' is probably an abbreviation of Latin *bacca*, a berry, while the term 'sweet' was once widely applied to plants with aromatic foliage. In France this tree is called *laurier* and in Germany *Lorbeerbaum*. Though often a shrub, it can grow fifty feet tall.

# Tree of Heaven

*Ailanthus altissima*      SIMAROUBACEAE

This handsome Chinese tree (Plate 64) has been widely planted in the south of England, especially around London and in other towns, where it stands the smoke well. In summer you can tell it by its enormous, pinnately compound leaves, often over a foot long, with from thirteen to twenty-five leaflets. They are like those of ash but are alternately placed on the twigs,

10

and each leaflet has a pointed tip and a broad base, bearing two small glands (p. 25). When the leaves open in May they show lovely bronze or crimson tints. In winter the exceptionally stout twigs, bearing small rounded buds above large leaf scars, mark it out (p. 46). The bark is black with a network of paler fissures. The trunk breaks up into ascending branches, which may reach a height of ninety-five feet, as at Endsleigh in Devon, while a girth of fourteen feet has been measured at Halstead in Essex.

The flowers of the Tree of Heaven are greenish in colour and only attract notice because they are borne in large bunches and have often a sharp unpleasant smell. Each bunch is either male or female, and as a rule a whole tree bears flowers of one sex only, though some trees show both sexes. Each flower has about five sepals, five greenish-white petals and either ten stamens or a five-celled pistil; they bear ample nectar and attract bees. After blossoming in July, the fruits ripen rapidly, and before the leaves fall in October the whole crown of foliage is decked with a glorious display of golden or orange-red ripening seeds. When the seeds fall, each is seen to be a hard black grain at the centre of a curiously twisted, papery wing; the twist gives it a spinning motion as it comes down and helps the wind to carry it far afield.

When the seed germinates next spring two yellowish-green seed-leaves are lifted, along with part of the wing, on a slender stem. The first true leaves have only three leaflets. The roots are apt to send up sucker shoots which are often used to propagate the tree. The early leaves on suckers, and on vigorous stems generally, are strikingly large, often eighteen inches long. When the leaves fade in autumn the leaflets drop off first; the long main stalk falls later. The pale brown wood is used in China for furniture and joinery.

The Tree of Heaven is not considered hardy in the north, but in central and southern Europe, and also in America, it is well established and occasionally naturalized. It was introduced from China in 1751, by Père Nicholas d'Incarville, a

BOX 137

Jesuit missionary at Peking. Its name is a translation of the Indonesian name of a related tree which grows in Amboyna, and means a tree that reaches to the skies; originally *ailanto*, it was Latinized as *ailanthus*. *Altissima* means 'highest of all'. The Germans call it *Götterbaum*, tree of the gods, and the French name is *vernis du Japon*.

# Box

*Buxus sempervirens*                                            BUXACEAE

Box Hill, a steep chalk bluff rising above the River Mole close to Dorking in Surrey, is the only place where you will find the box tree growing wild in abundance. But it also grows at Boxwell in Gloucestershire and was found in the past at Chequers in Buckinghamshire and Boxley in Kent. This is a curious distribution for a tree that has not been noted wild elsewhere, though all these places are in the south of England, and all have chalk or limestone soils. Some writers have suggested that box may have been introduced by the Romans, yet on the other hand it is quite usual to find a plant in small, scattered areas, on ground specially suited to it, near the limit of its natural range. Evidently the Anglo-Saxons, who named these places, recognized it as something unusual. Our name 'box' resembles Latin *buxus*, as do the French *buis* and the German *Buchs*; *sempervirens* means evergreen, and refers to the foliage.

The main home of the box tree lies around the Mediterranean Sea, but it also occurs in Switzerland and southern Germany.

Box foliage is made up of many small oval leathery leaves set in opposite pairs, each leaf being about three quarters of an inch long. They are dark green, smooth and shiny above but somewhat paler below, and have an odd musty smell. The twigs are fine and close-set, and the buds very small. Box flowers open from January to May, but rarely attract attention, since they are small, greenish, and set in the leaf axils. Each cluster holds both male and female flowers. Male flowers have

four whitish-green petals and four stamens; female flowers
have from four to twelve petals and a three-celled ovary.

The fruits, which ripen in October, are white papery pods,
about half an inch long, with three double-pointed horns.
They have three cells, each holding a few hard black seeds

**Box**
A, male flowers; B, female flower

which are blown away when the pod opens. The seedlings
have at first two thin deciduous seed-leaves, then normal
evergreen true leaves.

On Box Hill there are many slender trees up to thirty-five

feet tall and three feet round (Plate 65), with plentiful seedlings
below them, but nowhere does box make a big tree. In gardens
a dwarf variety which seldom flowers, but which is increased
by cuttings, is grown as low hedges which stand clipping
remarkably well. Occasionally taller trees are trained into
particular shapes, by topiary. The bark is grey and fine-grained,
though not quite smooth.

Box timber is quite distinct from all others, being golden in
colour, very smooth, hard, dense and heavy; even when
seasoned it does not float. It is also stable, changing in shape
very little. These properties ensure its use, despite its small
size, in rulers, mathematical instruments, and fine turnery and
carved work, particularly for chessmen. Infinitely fine carving
of statuettes, especially religious figures, was done in boxwood
by medieval craftsmen. More practical uses are as weavers'
shuttles, reels, bobbins, spindles, rolling-pins, pestles and
wooden screws; but boxwood is so scarce and costly that it
has been displaced, for most of these purposes, by other timbers.

About the year 1790 the Northumbrian artist and naturalist,
John Bewick, pioneered the use of boxwood for wood en-
gravings, a great advance on the cruder wood-cuts formerly
used. This process remained popular until displaced by
photographic methods, and it is still used, despite the exacting
labour involved, by a few modern artists. Every detail of each
picture must be engraved with a fine tool on the end-grain of
the box; this means that the thin trunk must be cut across,
and the small sections either used for equally small pictures
or assembled into larger composite blocks. End-grain blocks
have remarkable wearing properties and will print several
hundred thousand copies.

# Elms

*Ulmus* species                                    ULMACEAE

The elms are a distinctive, yet also a very variable group of
tall timber trees, which flourish all over Europe, Asia and

North America, except for the far north. In leaf, they are easily told apart from all other trees by their oblique or uneven leaf base (p. 143). This one-sidedness takes varied forms, such as a lobe, a twist or a cutting-short of one side but not the other. Its degree varies from one tree to another and even between leaves on the same branch, so it does not, as some books suggest, help you to tell one elm from another. The elm leaf is simple, more or less oval, and has a short stalk, a much-toothed edge and a fine point. Leaves are always alternately placed along the twigs, and in most elms they have a distinctly rough surface on both sides. The brownish-grey winter twigs, which may be smooth or hairy, follow a zig-zag trend from one alternate bud to another. The buds, which are oval, end in a blunt point and show several scales; their blackish-red colour is distinctive and they sit on distinct ledges (p. 48).

Elm bark, smooth at first, later becomes rough and grey; on some elms it is broken into squares, on others into a diamond-shaped pattern of ribs and fissures (Plates 69, 74). The sapwood is thin and pale cream to white. The heartwood is a rich reddish-brown and shows, on close inspection, a pretty pattern not seen on any other common timber. The pores are scattered through it in irregular groups, with the larger ones of each spring's growth set near the start of the annual ring, and the smaller ones, formed in summer, set further out, but always to one side. This pattern gives elm a lively grain, which, when seen on certain surfaces, has been likened to the feathers on the breast of a partridge. It may also be linked to elm timber's most unusual and useful feature—its interlocked grain. Elm logs cannot be split or cleft downwards like those of other trees for the fibres cling together and stop the tool. For this reason elm has many peculiar uses, such as chair seats and the hubs of wooden wheels; when the chair legs or wheel spokes are driven home, elm does not split as other timbers would do. Elm is also used for rollers, cable drums, boxes for metal goods and the bobbins on big fishing nets, because small pieces will withstand great strain and heavy wear without splitting.

Other uses of elm are related to its general strength and ready supply in big sizes; thus it is a good and attractive furniture wood. Elm is employed for outdoor furniture and to give waney-edged planks for barns. It is the traditional timber for coffins. Formerly it was used for the keels of big ships, and whole trunks were bored out to make water-mains, troughs and pumps. As long as it was always kept wet it lasted well, but so would any other timber; the reason that elm was specially chosen for these purposes was on account of the great size of individual trees. If elm is exposed to moisture where air is freely available too, as in a fence post, it proves a perishable timber. Elm refuses to burn until well-seasoned, and then burns slowly, though steadily.

The flowers of elm open before its leaves, in late February or early March. They can then be seen as a purplish haze among the bare branches. Closer inspection shows that the twigs carry dense clusters of tiny short-stalked flowers, with those of each cluster springing from a base, previously a flower-bud, at an angle of the twig. Each flower has three basal green bracts and a green calyx with about six lobes. Within this stand about six stamens with the purple anthers that give the flowers their main colour. Within these again is a one-celled pistil with two stigmas. Pollination is by wind. The fruits ripen in May and appear as greenish-yellow clusters above the foliage, often so bright that they are mistaken for flowers. Each separate fruit consists of a broad flat papery wing, near the centre of which stands a tiny seed.

The seeds are wind-borne. Despite their small size they attract birds and also squirrels. Most of the seeds fall while still green, and these only sprout if they reach moist bare earth within a few days of falling, and even so a high proportion prove infertile. Seed that ripens fully and becomes brown does not sprout until next spring. The seedling raises a pair of seed-leaves, each with a curious notch at the base, on a slender stalk; the first pair of true leaves are opposite, and deeply toothed.

Most, though not all elms send up large numbers of sucker shoots from their roots, particularly after the felling of a main stem. This can prove a nuisance in gardens, but it helps the trees to survive along the hedgerows. Every suckering elm is liable to surround itself with a thicket of younger trees. Those that come up in fields are eaten by livestock or destroyed by ploughing; but those in hedges are protected by the thorns of the hawthorn bushes and so have a fair chance of survival. Elms have a reputation, not altogether deserved, for being dangerous trees. One reason for this is that they are often left standing in suburban areas, long past their prime; but outwardly healthy elms will, very occasionally, shed large branches in midsummer, on still days and without warning.

*Ulmus* was the Roman name for the elm, and similar words occur in many European tongues—French *orme*, German *Ulme*, Dutch *olme*, and Swedish and Danish *elm*. The Anglo-Saxon name was *aelm*, and the word 'elm' is found in many place-names, such as Elmstead in Kent. *Fhalm* is recorded in Gaelic and *ailm* in Irish. The Welsh name is *llwyfanen*. The usual Gaelic is *leamhan;* it is found in place-names in the form 'leven', close to its actual pronunciation, such as Loch Leven in Fife, also Loch Leven in Argyll, and the River Leven in Dunbartonshire, Scotland. *Leaman* is its Irish form. In German the elm is also called *Rüster* while in Holland a common name is *iep*, which can also mean yew. An old English name was 'wych', hence Wychwood Forest in Oxfordshire; perhaps it only meant Wych elm, but at this date we cannot be sure.

## Wych Elm

Many features distinguish Wych elm, *Ulmus glabra*, from other elms that grow in Britain. Its leaf is larger, and broadens out towards the tip, then narrows suddenly. Sometimes the broad tip bears two subsidiary points besides the main one. The twigs are much stouter than those of other elms, and carry large chocolate-brown buds, rather rounded at their tips. The bark develops a clear network of ribs and fissures, sometimes spirally twisted (Plate 69). The tree has a graceful, open branching habit (Plates 67, 68), and its trunk divides quite low down into spreading branches. The seeds are larger than those of other elms, and are set in the centre of

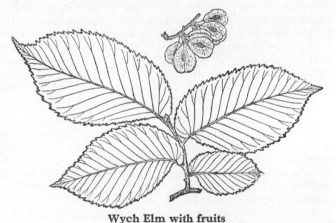

**Wych Elm with fruits**

the broad wing. Suckers are rarely produced even if a tree is cut down, and reproduction is almost entirely by seed. Foresters usually gather this as it ripens in May, and sow it at once.

The timber of Wych elm is considered more supple and springy than that of other elms; in fact the word 'wych' means pliant and bendable. It is used in furniture-making and boat-building.

Wych elm is the hardiest of our elms, and flourishes from the Highlands of Scotland to the south-east of England, and also in Ireland. It is the commonest sort in the northern and western uplands, though everywhere it thrives better down in the valleys, on well-watered fertile soil, rather than on hilltops. Its range on the Continent extends well into Norway, and also far up the Alps. Wych elm has grown in Britain since about 7000 B.C. Nowadays little is planted for timber, but Wych elm is a widely used ornamental tree in the north; in Edinburgh, for example, it is the leading street and park tree.

The scientific name of Wych elm is *Ulmus glabra*, the smooth elm—actually its leaves are very rough on their upper surface and downy underneath. A weeping form, var. *pendula*, is often grown in gardens, being grafted on a common stock; it bears seed profusely. Our biggest Wych elms are in Suffolk, one at Earl Soham being 138 feet high and another at Monks Eleigh twenty-five feet round. In France this tree is called *orme des montagnes*, in Germany *Bergulme*, both meaning mountain elm. In Denmark it is the *storbladet*, or large-leaved, *elm*.

### English Elm

This truly magnificent tree is native only to England, where it reaches its best development on heavy clay soils in the warm south-east. The mature tree (Plates 70, 73) has a sturdy upright trunk which bears stout branches in groups so that the foliage stands out from the trunk in great cloud-like masses. The bark is typically rough, splitting into square plates (Plate 74) and the individual twigs are very fine. The seeds are small, and set in the upper half of the wing; they are seldom fertile, and regrowth is mainly from abundant suckers. The botanical name of this tree is *Ulmus procera*, meaning the giant elm, and it apparently arose in the southern Midlands; it has since been widely planted elsewhere. On fertile land, in full sunlight it grows rapidly and shows good timber form. There is a tree 141 feet high at Syon House in Middlesex, and another thirty-one feet round at East Bergholt in Suffolk.

### Regional Elms

The Wych elm and the English elm are well-defined trees, but there are also many other forms of elm growing wild or cultivated along the hedgerows in various parts of England, Wales and the Channel Islands. These varieties shade into one another by slight degrees, and it is only fair to tell the reader that, although several experts have attempted to classify them, most published descriptions are more confusing than helpful. Distinctions based on leaf size, the shape of the leaf

**English Elm with fruits**

or the leaf-base, and the hairiness or otherwise of the twigs are of little value in the field, since most of the variations between 'species', so carefully described and illustrated, can be found, or at least imagined, on one and the same tree. Further, the scientific names recommended vary from one authority to the next and the English names are of little help; in particular, the term 'Dutch elm' is applied by countrymen to any unusual kind in the district concerned. Again statements that a particular regional race of elm yields a better timber than another have to be treated with reserve because merchants who buy hedgerow timber only get odd lots at odd times, and seldom handle fair samples of several races.

Some of these regional races are held to be varieties or hybrids of the Smooth-leaved elm, *Ulmus carpinifolia*, which is widely distributed on the Continent. Its typical form, which grows in our eastern counties, has slender leaves which are smooth and shining above and have long stalks; *carpinifolia* means 'hornbeam-leaved', and there is a slight resemblance to the leaves of that tree, but in the elm the two sides of the leaf are, as always, markedly uneven. The twigs often bear marked corky ribs. A Smooth-leaved elm at Dunmow in Essex scales 141 feet, and another at Great Waltham, Essex, is twenty-four feet round.

The general terms used for this and similar elms on the Continent are: in France, *orme champêtre*, and in Germany *Feldulme*, both meaning field elm; and in Denmark *småbladet*, or small-leaved, *elm*.

It has often been said that our peculiar British local races were introduced from the Continent, and of course people do, from time to time, import elms for planting. But many of them have not been found outside Britain so it is clear that these have developed here. The prehistoric pollen records show that elms were very common trees from 6000 to about 2500 B.C. A decline then set in, at just about the time when the first Neolithic farmers began to settle in Britain. Elm foliage is particularly palatable to livestock, and even today goat-keepers use it as fodder, while hungry horses nibble elm bark. The settlers had thus a special inducement to clear elm woods early, besides the fact that they grew on fertile, well-drained ground. The grazing beasts checked all regrowth from suckers, and under the systems of open-field agriculture and common grazing that ensued, elm became a scarce and local tree, surviving in the well-farmed lowlands only on odd patches of rough ground. Such conditions of isolation favour the development of peculiar local races in any plant or animal.

When the great enclosure movement got under way in the eighteenth century, thousands of elms were planted at intervals along the hedges to ensure supplies of timber. Landowners drew these trees from local nurseries—and records of many such sales survive. As a result, local races were multiplied and spread over wider areas, and they have since flourished along the hedgerows, renewing their particular strain by sucker shoots. The modern tendency is to regard these trees as clones (see p. 147) rather than as species.

Only two of these regional elms are commonly planted today, and though they are hard to tell apart they both look different to all other elms. They have a fine, upright columnar habit of growth, with a clear main stem and small side branches. This makes them suitable for street planting, especially as there is no risk of heavy side branches falling. One is the Cornish elm, *Ulmus stricta* var. *cornubiensis*, and the other is the Jersey elm, which has somewhat rounder leaves and a broader, somewhat pyramidal crown. It is found on all the larger Channel Islands and its scientific name, *U. stricta* var. *sarniensis*, is based on Sarnia, the Roman name for Guernsey; *stricta* means 'narrow-crowned'.

Elms thrive on islands and on exposed peninsulas like Cornwall, Selsey and Thanet, because their foliage is resistant to salt-laden sea gales.

On the Continent a common and conspicuous elm is the Fluttering elm, *Ulmus laevis*, which has its flowers and fruits in clusters, each on a long stalk, and which flutter in the wind. Its German name is *Flatterulme*, and the French is *orme diffus*.

Between 1927 and 1962, the elms of England appeared to be seriously threatened by the Dutch elm disease, caused by the fungus *Ceratostomella ulmi*, which is carried from ailing to healthy trees by the bark beetle *Scolytus scolytus*. In Holland nearly all the elms had been propagated from a single race, *Ulmus* × *hollandica* var. *belgica*; this had no resistance to the disease and so nearly all the Dutch elms died. In England the susceptible elms were soon attacked and killed also, but we have many races and most are resistant. With us, the disease has now died down, and young elms of the surviving strains may safely be planted again.

# Mulberry

*Morus nigra*                                        MORACEAE

King James I of England is usually credited with the introduction of the mulberry tree to Britain as part of a grand scheme to feed silkworms on its leaves and so promote a home silk industry. Actually it was established well before his day, and may in fact be a Roman introduction: the Saxons knew a 'more-beam' tree, a name based no doubt on the Roman *morus* which is the source of French *murier*, but we draw our modern name of mulberry from German *Maulbeere*. Yet this tree has never become naturalized, and you will find it only within gardens, grown for its acid pulpy fruits (Plate 75).

Mulberry is easily known in winter by its prominent bud scars, which are triangular in outline and stand out on alternate sides of the twig, facing out at right angles to its main trend. The buds sit on distinct ledges above them, and are chocolate brown in colour and conical in shape. The bark is pinkish-brown and becomes rough and scaly on old trees. The wood has a pale yellow sapwood and a deep yellow heart. Being small, it is used only for decorative carving or cabinet work. It burns well. The leaves are heart-shaped, with toothed edges and a rough surface. They are dark green in colour (Plate 76).

Mulberry flowers sometimes appear with both sexes on one tree, but more often they are on separate male and female trees. Edible fruit is produced without pollination. Male flowers are borne in green catkins, about an inch long, on short stalks. Each flower has four sepals and four stamens, which scatter pollen on the wind. The female catkins are shorter. Each green flower has four bracts and one pistil. The berry is actually a group of fruits arising from the numerous flowers of one female catkin; yet it looks just like a raspberry—which is the fruit of a single flower—being red in colour and oval. Each segment of it has a mass of pulp surrounding a single seed. The berries ripen in July, and have a refreshing acid-sweet taste. They soon fall or are knocked down by birds, which scatter the seeds. The seedling which arises next spring is at first tiny; it has two oval seed-leaves, followed by wavy-edged juvenile leaves, and then normal foliage. A mulberry tree at Myddleton Hall in Middlesex is forty-eight feet tall and eight feet round. Mulberry is considered native to Central Asia.

# Plane

*Platanus acerifolia*                          PLATANACEAE

The plane tree that beautifies the parks, squares and streets of London, Paris and many other large cities is a hybrid between two wild kinds, the Oriental plane of Asia Minor, *Platanus orientalis*, and the North American plane, *P. occidentalis*. Neither of these species grows well in northern Europe, but the hybrid between them shows remarkable vigour and tolerance of town conditions. It is believed to have arisen accidentally about 1670 at Oxford. As a rule it is increased by cuttings, though it occasionally sets fertile seed.

The peculiar bark is a sure guide to this tree, for as fresh layers are formed patches break off on the surface, giving a pretty dappled pattern of pale yellow on a dark brown back-ground (Plate 79). Although the point is sometimes disputed, this bark-shedding habit is a great help to a tree growing in a smoky atmosphere. All tree trunks breathe through their bark, and can do so more freely if their pores are not clogged with soot. The winter buds are remarkable in being cone-shaped, and covered by a single scale which is almost completely surrounded by the scar of last year's fallen leaf (p. 45).

Plane buds and leaves are always alternately placed, a fact

that distinguishes the leaf from the similar one of the sycamore. Each leaf has a long stalk with a hollow at the base, which hides next year's bud beneath it. The leaf blade is divided into five broad lobes, in a palmate fashion; when it first opens it bears a coating of brown hairs.

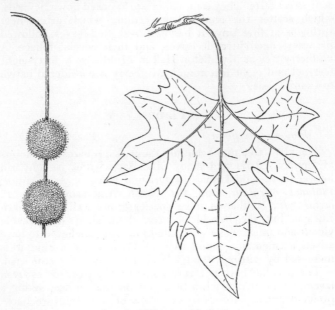

**London Plane with fruits**

Plane flowers and seeds are produced in curious round structures that dangle from long stalks, two or three at intervals down the same stalk. Best described as 'bobbles', they have earned the tree its American name of buttonwood. Botanically they are catkins, and each is made up of a large number of small green flowers radiating from a central base, so producing the globe. Male and female catkins appear on the same branch, and pollination is by wind. Each little yellowish-green male flower consists of four upright anthers grouped round a narrow, flat-topped column called a 'connective', with a ring of four tiny sepals and four petals at its base. Each female flower is made up of clusters of pistils, with crimson styles projecting, so that it looks reddish-green; it has a similar ring of sepals and petals at its foot. The female catkins are smaller and look more shaggy than the male ones; as they ripen, the separate pistils become more obvious. By midwinter they have matured to brown, somewhat woody structures which slowly break up and release scores of tiny brown seeds, each with a tuft of short sharp hairs, and a spiky stalk. The woody 'core' is left on the tree. A plane seedling is something of a find. It has two long narrow seed-leaves, arched over so that they look like the blades of scimitars. These are followed by oval leaves, then normal lobed ones.

The Greeks called this tree *platanos*, from *platos*, meaning broad, because of its broad leaf. The Romans altered this to *platanus*, which is the root of most of the modern names; *acerifolia* means 'having leaves like a sycamore'. In France and Germany the plane is called *platane*, in Holland *plataan*, and in Scandinavia *platan*. Note carefully, however, that in America it is called 'sycamore' or buttonwood; whilst in Scotland the name 'plane' is widely used for the English sycamore tree, *Acer pseudoplatanus* (p. 71).

As planes are grown almost entirely for ornament, little timber becomes available. The wood is pinkish-brown, without distinct heart, and has a general resemblance to beech. If it is cut on the tangent its rays make an intricate and attractive pattern; thin veneers made in this way are called 'lacewood' and are used on fine furniture.

Plane has found favour as a decorative tree because of its pleasing light green foliage and gay bark pattern, and because it casts a cool deep shade in summer. Further, it stands pruning well. Fine specimens are shown in Plates 77 and 78, and the winter aspect reveals the curly upper branches typical of this tree. It is a long-lived tree, and the big planes in Berkeley Square, London, are nearly 200 years old. The tallest recorded tree is at Carshalton in Surrey, which scales 125 feet; the stoutest, at the Bishop's Palace, Ely, is twenty-six feet round, and was probably planted about 1680.

# Walnut

*Juglans regia*                                       Juglandaceae

Walnut forms a handsome tree with bold masses of foliage, carried on stout branches that spread out in a characteristic upward-trending pattern (Plate 80). Its winter twigs are very stout, with small round black buds and distinct, large, horse-shoe-shaped leaf scars (p. 45). If you cut them across on the slant with a sharp knife you will see that the pith is 'chambered', a feature found in no other tree; it has thin plates across it, with hollows between, and the whole structure has a resemblance to a little ladder. Buds and leaves are always alternately arranged.

Walnut leaves are large, long-stalked and pinnately compound, often over eight inches long, with about seven leaflets. The end leaflet is larger than the rest, and those at the base are the smallest. If you crush a leaf you will at once smell the rich, fruity aroma peculiar to this tree. The juice of the leaves may stain your fingers brown; it was used by gypsies as a sun-tan lotion to make their faces darker. The bark is a pale ash grey, and on old trees a network of deep hollows develops, with irregular flat plates between them (Plate 81).

Walnut trees rarely flower until the tree is about fifteen years old and well established; they then start to bear green, wind-pollinated catkins. Both sexes are produced on the same branch, the female flowers right at the tip, the male ones farther back, in separate structures of very different appearance. The male catkins are curved, slender objects, about the shape and size of a fat caterpillar. They are made up of many small simple flowers, each being comprised of one bract, two bracteoles, four sepals and ten to twenty stamens. Female flowers are solitary or in clusters of two to four; they are green, flask-shaped, and stand on short stalks. A green calyx surrounds a one-celled ovary, and bears four bracts at its tip close to a

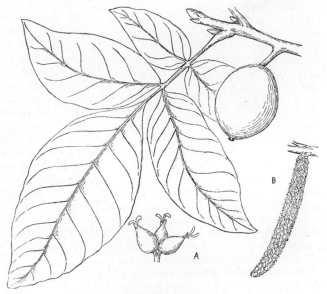

**Walnut in fruit**
A, female flowers; B, male flowers

pair of purple stigmas, reflexed so as to look like a fork. These flowers, about half-an-inch long at first, expand and develop remarkably through the summer. By August they have become oval fruits as big as a plum, with a soft pulp surrounding a soft-shelled nut (Plate 92). At this stage many are gathered and pickled in vinegar as a seasoning. Green walnuts attract large-beaked birds—especially rooks—and also squirrels. Those left on the tree gradually lose their green outer pulp, while the shell within it becomes hard and woody. By October the typical crinkly, light brown shell of the nut is fully exposed and it soon falls. The two halves of the shell have a prominent join, raised to form a rib.

Walnuts are produced plentifully in south and central Europe where the tree is grown commercially in orchards. Choice strains which fruit freely are often grafted on the common stock. In the north seed-bearing is less regular and ample. When you crack a walnut you see within the husk two large fleshy seed-leaves which appear to be separated by a papery brown partition but are always joined at one point. If you sow a whole nut in spring, these seed-leaves remain within the shell and a stout shoot appears, which bears at first small scale-like leaves, and then compound leaves with toothed leaflet edges and pointed leaflet tips, before normal leaves appear. In nature the nuts are spread by birds and squirrels, who do not eat all they gather. So walnut trees sometimes spring up naturally in hedgerows or on waste ground where nobody would plant them. The kernel—that is, the two seed-leaves—is both deliciously flavoured and highly nutritious, being rich in oil and protein. It tastes good raw and is widely used in cookery and confectionery. Its surface is yellowish-brown, and the flesh white.

The sapwood of walnut is broad and pale greyish-brown. The heartwood within it is a rich greyish-brown to chocolate colour, but shades towards black, greenish, yellowish or reddish tints. These colour variations flow over the surface, regardless of the annual rings, producing beautiful, lively mottled effects. Large walnut trunks therefore fetch very high prices for cutting into decorative veneers for furniture, radio cabinets, etc. The wood of smaller stems is used for attractive carvings, bowls, spoons, breadboards and similar luxury woodware. It is the favoured timber for gun stocks because it is robust and never changes shape when seasoned. It is naturally durable and burns well, though of course such valuable stuff is seldom used out of doors or for firewood.

Walnut is never seen as a forest tree in northern Europe, but is widely grown as an orchard or wayside one, spaced well apart so that each gets full sun to ripen good nut crops. Our tallest walnut, eighty-two feet, is at Laverstoke Park in Hampshire, and our stoutest, twenty-one and a half feet, at Pilton Church, Northamptonshire; but most big trees are felled for veneer timber.

The Roman name of *juglans* is regarded as a corruption of *Jovis glans*, the nut of the god Jupiter; *regia* means royal, fit for a king. The French call is simply *noyer*, the nut tree (the nut itself being *noix*). It was introduced, probably by the Romans, to the northerly lands of Europe where it is called in various tongues 'the foreign nut'. Thus, in England it is walnut, or in the south-west, welshnut, from Saxon *wealh*, foreign; in Germany *Walnuss* or *Welchnuss*; in Holland *walnoot*; in Denmark *valnød*; and in Sweden *valnot*. Celtic names are the Welsh *cnauen ffrengig*, French nut, and Irish *gallcno*, with the same meaning.

# Birch

*Betula* species                    BETULACEAE

The white bark of the graceful birches marks them out from most other trees (Plates 82, 83); only the White poplar can sometimes show a resemblance. The very thin whippy twigs of the birch are, however, a feature that no other tree can equal. If we look closely at these twigs we find that their young bark is not white but purplish-brown; the white bark is developed later, as the twigs grow into stout branches and trunks, by the activity of the bark cambium. On old trees this cambial growth becomes less regular, and patches of dark grey or black bark, sometimes quite rugged, result (Plate 84). Birch bark is tough and had many uses in the past, including round boxes, plates and roof shingles, since it is waterproof.

It is rich in tannin, which tans hides to a soft leather. If heated carefully it exudes a gum, and the Mesolithic people who lived about 5000 B.C. at Starr Carr near Scarborough in Yorkshire, used this unlikely material to fix flint blades to wooden handles. It also provides an oil for dressing leather. In Canada the bark of the Paper birch, *Betula papyrifera*, is used by the Indians for birch bark canoes. In Switzerland the mountaineers make alp-horns with strips of birch bark. The bark of fallen birch trees resists decay, persisting on the forest floor longer than the tree's wood does.

In winter the birch bears small, alternately set, many-scaled and pointed buds (p. 51) and also the well-formed male catkins. In April the leaves expand, each with a short stalk and a toothed edge; they are roughly triangular in shape, sometimes approaching a diamond or oval outline, and always end in a point. At the same time the male catkins expand and droop downwards. Each consists of numerous bracts, each main bract carrying two smaller bracteoles and three flowers that have in turn two still smaller petals and two stamens to shed pollen (Plate 85). The female catkins are now seen as slender upright structures. Their rough olive-green surface is built up of many bracts, with purple stigmas protruding to catch the pollen. The arrangement of bracts and flowers resembles that of the male catkin, but each flower is simply a two-celled ovary with two stigmas.

During the summer the female catkins enlarge and start to droop, eventually becoming about one and a half inches long and a quarter of an inch in diameter. In autumn, when the leaves are fading to gold and falling fast, these catkins break up. Both bracts and seeds fall away from a fine central stalk, the bracts now appearing as three-pointed scales. Each seed is an extremely small nut bearing two little wings. It takes about two million birch seeds to weigh one pound. Being small and winged, they are carried by the winds over great distances, and nearly all the birches you see in the woods have arisen naturally from such wind-borne seeds. Next spring they germinate, putting forth two minute oval seed-leaves, then three-pointed first true leaves. Normal leaves follow, and provided the little seedling escapes smothering by weeds or biting by animals, it grows remarkably fast. Birch is often grown for ornamental planting, but in the woods the forester finds more than enough without planting any.

Birch trees will only develop in full light, but they are very hardy, resisting frost, sun and wind. Foresters regard them as 'pioneer' trees, adapted to colonize land; but they are relatively short-lived, seldom reaching 100 years, and their place is then often taken by longer-lived, slower-growing, 'successor' trees. Birch is valued because it acts as a 'nurse' which aids the establishment of more valuable kinds, such as beech, hemlock and Douglas fir, which benefit from shelter in youth. Often these are planted below a light cover of natural birch, which is removed later. Birch was the first tree to spread over Britain when the glaciers receded about 12,000 B.C. On the Continent it goes to the farthest north, right to the tundra, and far up the mountain ranges. In the Scottish Highlands the wild birchwoods are valued by sheep farmers because they give shelter and some grazing to their flocks when blizzards sweep the hills; but most trees are of poor quality through cutting over for fuel and tanbark in the past, leaving rugged coppice stems marred by browsing in their youth.

The wood of birch is very pale brown or cream in colour, with a dull surface, no clear heartwood, and no distinguishing features. It is hard, strong, and works well, but does not last out of doors. It is widely used in turneries to provide small, cheap but serviceable tool handles, broom heads, brush backs, toys and similar small objects; the biggest demand is for cotton reels, spools, bobbins, and shuttles for the textile trades. In Scandinavia, where the birch trees grow larger and are of better form than ours, it is widely used for furniture. A great deal of veneer is peeled from the stouter logs, and used as the two surface 'plies' of three-ply wood, with spruce wood between them. Occasional trees show an attractive figure, called *masur* or flamy birch, and this wood is highly prized for decorative veneers, high-grade furniture, and the carving or turning of ornaments.

Birch is a very good firewood, and is the main winter fuel in the country districts of Scandinavia and central Europe

**Birch leaves and ripening female catkins**

where it is cut in summer and stacked below the eaves of the houses to season for the winter; it also gives good charcoal, and is a satisfactory wood for paper pulp. The twigs have many uses, as 'birches' for chastising schoolboys, besoms for sweeping leaves, steeplechase jumps and as a source of carbon in metal refining. They are also made up, with cleft timber, into faggots and firelighters. In spring the rising sap of birch trees is rich in sugar, and the trees are sometimes tapped for this 'syrup'; it can be fermented to make a wine, or evaporated to leave a sweet candy.

When birch buds expand they show a purplish bloom before the emerald leaflets unfold, and the woods have a resinous fragrance. A brilliant, though poisonous, fungus is associated with the birch, living in symbiosis with its roots. This is the mushroom-shaped Fly agaric, *Amanita muscaria*, or Pixie's Seat; it is bright scarlet, with white spots and a white stalk.

The names for birch in the Teutonic languages are much alike, being *birce* in Anglo-Saxon, *berk* in Dutch, *Birke* in German, *birk* in Danish, and *bjork* in Norwegian and in Swedish. In northern England and in Scotland the form 'birk' is usual; many place-names, old and new, throughout Britain, include the elements 'birk' or 'birch'; examples are Birks Bridge in Lancashire and Much Birch in Herefordshire. The Welsh name is *bedwen*, which gives the common place-name elements *bedw* and *fedw*, and also the Bedwyns—villages in Wiltshire. In Gaelic it is *bheith*, pronounced *vey*, giving Beith in Ayrshire and many names of woods in the Highlands. The Irish name is *beit*. The French call it *bouleau*, and the Finns *koivu*. *Betula* is the Roman name.

Two tall species of birch are native to Britain and Ireland; the terms 'silver birch' and 'white birch', and the obsolete scientific name *Betula alba*, have been applied to both of them, so they help us little. The Warty birch, *B. pendula* (= *B. verrucosa*) can be known by the presence of little warts or swellings on its twigs. Many beautiful weeping trees belong to this kind. *Pendula* means 'weeping' and *verrucosa* means 'warty'. The Hairy birch, *B. pubescens*, has downy twigs, and the bark on old trees peels away in strips; *pubescens* means 'hairy'. Both kinds are generally spread and may grow together in the same wood; only the Hairy and Dwarf birches, however, grow on the Shetland and Orkney Islands.

The British records for height and girth go to the Warty birch, being 102 feet tall at Woburn in Bedfordshire, and eleven and a half feet round at Worlingham in Suffolk.

The Dwarf birch, *Betula nana* (*nana* means 'dwarf'), is a shrubby species that can be told by its deeply indented leaf-edge and clear network of veins on the leaf's underside. It is found in the Scottish Highlands, being the commonest form along the north coast of Scotland, in Sutherland and Caithness, and on outlying islands; also on the northern tundras and high in the European mountains.

# Alder

*Alnus glutinosa*                                    BETULACEAE

Alder grows beside streams, ponds and lakes (Plate 86), but you are unlikely to find it anywhere else. It is easily known because its round leaves end in a shallow notch, not a tip. Its buds, borne alternately, are distinctly stalked and have a purple waxy bloom (p. 44). Trees of any size are sure to bear, at any time of the year, curious woody cones (Plate 103). On its roots alder bears curious nodules, like those of leguminous trees, in which lives a bacterium called *Schinzia alni*, which enables it to fix the nitrogen of the air. This may explain why ground on which alder grows, or has grown, is always fertile; though it does not colonize sour acid peat bogs, it thrives in fens where the water is almost stagnant.

Alder leaves are simple, alternate, dark green in colour and have a toothed edge; they hang on the tree late into autumn, then turn black before falling. This reveals the flowers already developed before winter begins. Both sexes are borne on the same branch and pollination is done by wind. The male flowers are borne in oblong catkins which are erect at first, but later become drooping; they are about an inch long and reddish-brown in colour. Many small flowers expand in each, being grouped in fours on short stalks below curious compound bracts; each separate flower has four sepals and four stamens which scatter clouds of golden pollen.

The female catkins are upright, purplish-brown and club-shaped. They consist of many bracts bearing pairs of flowers, each having an ovary and two stigmas, but no other organs; each flower yields a single seed. After pollination, the female catkins become green and enlarged, assuming an oval or spherical shape. Their bracts become woody and eventually brown in colour, forming a cone. During the winter this cone

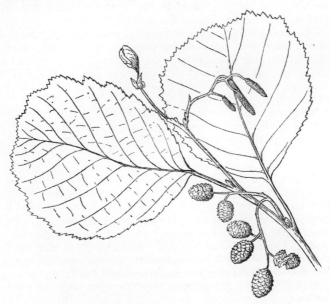

**Alder, with stalked bud, male catkins and cones**

opens, and the seeds escape from the gaps between the bracts. These seeds are very numerous and very small. Each consists of a little nut with two hollow wings, one on either side; the wings help the seed to travel through the air, and also keep it afloat if it lands on the water.

In nature alder springs up mainly from seeds that have

drifted, during winter floods, on to bare mud banks, or streamsides from which the water later recedes. Under cultivation it is easily raised, provided the nursery bed has been inoculated with soil from an alder marsh to supply the helpful bacterium, *Schinzia alni*, and is kept damp. The seedling has two oval seed-leaves, then curious lobed and pointed early leaves, before the usual leaf appears.

Once established, alder is very tenacious of life and will shoot again after repeated cuttings. Along our streams the alder roots play a useful part in holding up the banks and stopping erosion. Though it sometimes gets in the way of drainage machinery or fishermen's rods, it is a mistake to try to remove it completely.

The bark is dark brown to black, and bears, on old trees, a pattern of shallow squares. Its underside holds a vivid orange dye, though the actual wood is white when freshly felled. The wood later changes to a warm pinkish-brown with no clear heartwood. It is firm and smooth but relatively soft, qualities which fit it for coarse turnery and carving. Most alder poles today go to turneries to be made into broom heads and cheap tool handles. An important use in the past was as soles for clogs, a tough shoe worn particularly in Lancashire, which has leather uppers, a wooden base and iron bearing-strips below. The soles were roughly cut to shape in the woods, stacked to season and later carved to suit the wearer's foot by the clog-maker. Though a poor firewood, alder yields good charcoal, and the old gunpowder mills were built near alder swamps.

Both turnery poles and clog soles are obtained from coppiced alders, cut back repeatedly and left to sprout again. This, together with occasional streamside clearances, explains why alder is usually seen as a much-divided, bushy tree. Left to itself, it can grow seventy feet tall and twelve feet in girth, as recorded at Fairlawne, Tonbridge, Kent.

The Romans called this tree *alnus*, a word related to the modern French *aune*. The specific name, *glutinosa*, meaning sticky, refers to the surface of the young, newly opened leaves. The tree's names in Teutonic languages are varied but related, being *Erle* or *Eller* in German, *els* in Dutch, *el* in Danish, *al* in Swedish, and *al* or *or* in Norwegian. Our name 'alder' comes from Anglo-Saxon *aler*. Because alders only grow in marshy places, and also indicate fertile soil, good for settlement if not too damp, they figure very often in place-names. In Hampshire, Aldershot, meaning the alder wood, and Alresford, ford by the alders, come clearly from Anglo-Saxon. Ellerbeck—alder stream—in Yorkshire is from the Danish, 'eller' being the plural form of *el*; Allithwaite, from *aller tveit* meaning alder clearing, in Lancashire, has Norwegian origins. 'Orrell', compounded from Norse *or* and Danish *el*, is still used for the tree in the Forest of Dean, and there is a place called Orrell in Lancashire. The Norsemen called an alder-fen a *kjarr*, a name preserved in both English and Scottish place names, such as Carrbank in Westmorland and Carradale in Argyll. In Welsh the alder is *gwernen*, and a shortened form of this, *wern*, is applied to many marshy meadows. The Gaelic name is *fearn*, found in Ferness, meaning alder waterfalls, in Argyll; it is shortened to 'arn' in Scots, giving Arnwood and the 'arn-tree', still a local name for alder. In Ireland, where alder is common, it is called *fearnoge*.

Alder reached Britain long ago, about 5500 B.C., and can now be found in suitable moist spots almost everywhere in the British Isles, even far up into the hills. On the Continent its range extends from southern Norway, Sweden and Finland, south to Greece, and it thrives far up the mountains. Alder yields four dyes—tawny red from the bark, pink from the wood, green from the catkins and yellow from the young shoots.

The Grey alder, *Alnus incana*, is a related tree of more bushy form, distinguished by reddish-brown buds with rounded tips, downy twigs, stalkless cones, and oval leaves that end in a point and are somewhat hairy beneath. Very hardy, it is found from the North Cape of Norway throughout central Europe to the Alps. Springing freely from suckers, it is not destroyed by shifting rock or shingle. It thrives below glaciers, helps to stop avalanches, and is valued as a soil stabilizer for flood control. Occasionally it can be found in English woodlands, having been used as a possible 'nurse' for timber trees on exposed land. In Germany it is distinguished as *Grauerle*, grey alder, from the darker *Schwarzerle*, 'black alder'; in Scandinavia it is called *hvid-el*, white alder, to distinguish it from *rød-el*, 'red alder', so-called from the colour of the fresh-felled wood. Grey alder is also native to Canada and the United States. Our common alder has been introduced to America where it is called 'black alder'.

# Hornbeam

*Carpinus betulus*                                    BETULACEAE

A general resemblance of leaves, buds and bark often leads to confusion between hornbeam and beech, a much better-known tree, so it is as well to stress the points that mark the hornbeam out. Hornbeam leaves are oval, and about the same size as beech leaves, but their edges are doubly toothed, and their veins stand out strongly in parallel lines. The buds, brown and alternately set, are shorter than those of beech, and are slightly bent in towards the twig, like crouching mice (p. 51). The bark, smooth and grey like that of beech, is usually marked with a network of smooth lines, which shine with a metallic gleam, and the bole is nearly always fluted (Plate 88) and not truly round.

Both flowers and fruit are quite different from those of beech. In April, just before the leaves open, two kinds of catkins expand on the same branch; both are greenish since the hornbeam is wind-pollinated. The male catkins, borne on the previous year's twigs, are slender chains about one inch long; each separate flower consists of a single green bract and about ten stamens with conspicuous orange anthers. Female catkins are borne nearer the tips of the twigs, in shorter hanging clusters; they appear to be made up of green bracts with their tips recurved and pointing upwards. Examination will reveal, below each bract, a pair of smaller *bracteoles*, each with one long and two short points, and a pair of single-celled pistils, each ending in a long, finely-divided crimson style. The points of these styles collect the wind-blown pollen. Botanists regard

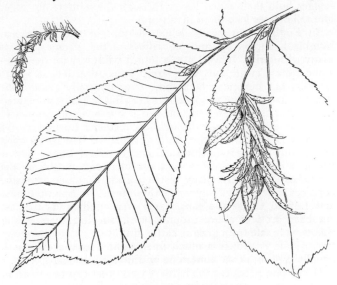

**Hornbeam;** male flowers above, fruits on right

one *bracteole*, plus one pistil, as one flower, so there are two flowers below each bract, but they remain united.

As the fruit ripens the *bracteoles* (not the bracts) expand into papery, green, three-pointed wings about an inch long, which fall away in pairs. They carry with them a pair of tiny ribbed green nuts, less than a quarter of an inch long. Though these hornbeam seeds are so small, they attract many small birds and also squirrels. Those that escape lie dormant on the forest floor for eighteen months before sprouting. Then they raise two oval seed-leaves above ground, and these are followed by heart-shaped early leaves with irregularly toothed edges, before normal leaves appear. Young hornbeam trees and hedges hold their faded leaves through the winter, but older and taller trees lose them in autumn.

In England hornbeam is native only in the south-east, roughly Kent, Sussex and the valleys of the Thames and its many tributaries. In Wales it is found wild only on the limestone near Cardiff and Chepstow. It is regarded as a late arrival from Europe, which came over naturally about 2500 B.C. and had no time to spread farther. But it has been planted throughout Britain and Ireland and is everywhere completely hardy. It is found wild throughout northern Europe, as far north as Denmark and the south of Sweden. It makes a good hedge, but is otherwise little cultivated today. In the past it was a valued source of firewood and charcoal, and of faggots for baker's ovens. In many districts near London, extensive coppices were formed to provide these fuels. At Epping Forest and Enfield Chase the hornbeams were pollarded, that is, cut back six feet above ground level, so that their young shoots were safe from grazing cattle, but open-grown unlopped trees (Plate 87) make a much finer sight. Hornbeam thrives equally well on chalk, limestone and non-limy soils.

Hornbeam produces the hardest wood that can be grown in Europe. It is very pale brown with no distinct heartwood, close-grained and heavy. It works well with sharp tools, giving a smooth finish, and wears very well indeed. Its uses have included wooden cogs and cams in machinery, particularly old-fashioned windmills and watermills; bench tops for heavy trades; wearing parts of pianos; yokes for the necks of draught oxen and the comely shoulders of dairymaids; mallets and beaters; rollers, tool handles, screws and pegs; skittles, skittle balls, chessmen and similar small objects. You are most likely to see it today as a chopping-block in your butcher's shop; many small pieces of hornbeam are glued and cramped together so that only the hardest end-grain appears on the surface which endures constant chopping without splintering, or blunting the edges of the cutting tools.

The name 'hornbeam' refers to the horny texture of the wood, and is obviously akin to German *Hornbaum*, both 'beam' and *Baum* meaning a tree. In France hornbeam bears the pleasing name of *charme*, while in Denmark it is *avnbøg*, in Norway *agnbok*, and in Sweden *avenbok*. *Carpinus* is the old Roman name, while *betulus* signifies 'birch tree'. The Welsh name is *oestrwydden*. Hornbeam can grow very tall, reaching 105 feet at Durdans near Epsom in Surrey, and also very stout, being seventeen and a half feet round at Hatfield Forest in Essex. Young seedlings spring up freely in woods where there is no grazing; it is easily raised from seed stored in moist sand for eighteen months after falling. Large trees still fetch good prices for specialized uses; the rollers that carry the rack-bench in a country sawmill are often hornbeam. Unfolding hornbeam leaves, bright green with pink bud-scales, are very pretty, while in autumn the fading leaves have an attractive golden stage.

# Hazel

*Corylus avellana*                              CORYLACEAE

Hazel is seen more often as a bush than a tree (Plate 89); it grows very freely indeed as coppice, sending up many strong shoots when cut back, and has been widely cultivated in this way. Occasionally it forms a low spreading tree about twelve feet high with a trunk a foot round. Its leaves, which are remarkably broad and end in a little short tip, make it easily known in summer; they have a short stalk, and are doubly toothed, the main points bearing smaller ones. In winter the round buds, which are brown at first but become green by February (p. 48), distinguish it; they are set alternately on distinctly hairy twigs. All through the winter many bushes bear conspicuous male catkins shaped like lamb's tails (Plate 90). These are formed in September, and in late February they expand to shed yellow pollen. They are made up of many flowers, each a single scale covering four stamens.

**Hazel in fruit**
Female catkins are shown on left, with male catkins below

The female flowers, set farther back on the branches, are far smaller. Each is a bud-shaped cluster of green bracts, at the tip of which you can see three crimson stigmas projecting from a one-celled pistil. During the summer the fruit develops into a hard-shelled, round nut, at first green but later dark

brown with a pale grey-brown circular base. At the same time
the bracts expand to form an irregular leafy cup, longer than
the nut. These fruits are the familiar hazel nuts, cob-nuts or
filberts of commerce, widely used in chocolates or eaten as
dessert. Some are grown in Britain, but most are imported
from southern Europe where selected strains of freely fruiting
hazel are grown, spaced well apart in orchard fashion.

Hazel nuts attract many birds and squirrels, besides small
boys, and their spread depends on chance losses. They sprout
freely next spring. The seed-leaves remain in the shell, and
the shoot that arises bears first scale leaves, then normal ones.
Most regrowth in the woods is by means of coppice shoots;
the roots never bear sucker shoots.

Hazel reached Britain about 8000 B.C. and soon became a
major shrub of the prehistoric broadleaved forests. Its pliable
stems, easily cut and worked, attracted early settlers who found
scores of uses for them, including fishing rods, traps for birds
and fish, spikes and rods for holding thatch to roofs, bonds for
tying bundles, stakes and binders for hedges, and tool handles.
The Neolithic people who lived in the Somerset marshes,
4,500 years ago, used bundles of hazel rods to carry tracks over
soft ground. Forked twigs make good divining rods, enabling
gifted people to detect underground sources of water.

As farming extended, hazel rods were found the best material
for weaving hurdles and temporary fences, widely used before
the days of stone walls, wire fences or hawthorn hedges. These
stock-proof barriers are made by the skilful interweaving of
hazel rods, some round, others cleft with the billhook into
two halves, in such a way that the whole structure binds itself
together. As natural supplies grew short, hazel coppices were
widely planted in the south of England, from about 1400 A.D.
onwards. Some are still managed for hazel rods, each section
being cut every seven years, but most are now uneconomic,
and their owners are replacing hazel with taller trees.

The coppices still supply all the pea sticks and bean rods we
need for our gardens. In the past they yielded faggots for

bakers' ovens and brick kilns. Another important product was wattle, interwoven cleft-hazel used to support clay walls in 'wattle-and-daub' buildings which had oaken frames and were often substantial structures. Hazel wood is mid-brown in colour, strong and hard, but not naturally durable; some is used for crate rods and clothes props. The bark is grey-brown and always very smooth, except for bands of cork-rimmed pores.

The name of hazel is much the same in all Teutonic languages: *haesil* in Anglo-Saxon; *hazelaar* in Dutch; *Hasel* in German and *hassel* in Scandinavian tongues. Haslemere, meaning hazel pond, in Surrey is an example of its frequent use in place names. *Corylus* and *avellana* are both Roman names for hazel. In France the bush is called *coudrier*, and also *noisetier* because it bears a nut named *noisette*. In Wales it is *collen*, and in Gaelic and Irish *cuillean*. Hazel is found all over the British Isles, including the Outer Hebrides and the Orkney and Shetland Islands.

# Oaks

*Quercus* species                                        FAGACEAE

Britain has two kinds of native oak (Plates 93, 94) but as they are much alike in many points, and as intermediate forms are very common, they will first be described together and their small points of difference discussed later. Both are long-established trees which have grown here since about 7000 B.C., and you can find both kinds growing, either wild or in cultivation, everywhere except on the more outlying islands. Oak, considered as a single kind of tree, far exceeds all others in abundance, and a review of the country's woodlands, hedgerow trees and timber reserves, carried out by the Forestry Commission in 1947, showed that at that date one third of all our trees were oaks.

Oak leaves are easily known by their wavy outline for they have an irregular series of lobes along either side (p. 34). When an oak tree is leafless in winter you can tell it by the arrangement of its buds, which are alternate along the twigs but grouped in a cluster near the tip of every twig (p. 47); all other trees with clustered buds show this plan on short shoots only. Oak bark, smooth and greyish-brown at first, soon becomes rugged, giving a rough grey bole that is often slightly buttressed at the foot (Plate 91). Due to the peculiar bud arrangement, an oak growing in the open develops a typically widely spread and much branched crown, but rarely grows very tall (Plate 93). In woodland, where the side branches become suppressed by the shade from surrounding trees, oak will soar to great heights and yield the fine straight bole that the timber merchant admires (Plate 94). Our tallest oak today, at Marchmont in Berwickshire, Scotland, reaches 128 feet and is of the pedunculate kind. The stoutest, an old pollard tree on Cilcochynyn Farm, Pontfadog, near Chirk in Denbighshire, North Wales, is forty-three feet round; it is a sessile oak.

Oak has separate male and female flowers both borne on the same tree (Plate 109); but often a summer may pass without any flowers appearing, even on a mature tree. The male catkins, borne in groups, have long stalks that carry, at close intervals, separate individual flowers, each with a bract at its base. Each flower has about six green sepals, and eight yellow stamens which shed abundant wind-borne pollen. These catkins as a whole appear yellowish-green when they open in May. The female catkins are much smaller and less obvious. Each catkin, which may or may not have a stalk, is a cluster of two or three green flowers. Each individual flower has one large bract at its base, and consists of a cluster of small bracteoles surrounding a one-celled pistil which bears three stigmas. During the summer these bracteoles become fused together, so forming the typical acorn cup; as it expands, it becomes hard and woody, and develops a knobbly greenish-brown outer surface. The fruit within it ripens into an oval nut with a hard smooth shell and a large white fleshy kernel which consists of two seed-leaves. This is the familiar acorn which is green at first but becomes brown, with a circular, pale grey base when fully ripe (Plate 114); the little spike at the tip is the remains of the stigma. As a rule the acorn falls from the cup, and lies on the forest floor to await dispersal by chance means.

Acorns are no good for people to eat because they are bitter and full of tannin. They attract sheep, horses, cattle and pigs, and in the past pigs were let loose in the oakwoods to fatten themselves on acorns; this custom, called 'pannage', still survives in the New and the Dean Forests. Other beasts and birds which seek out acorns greedily are wood pigeons, pheasants, partridges, wild ducks, rooks, jays, woodpeckers, badgers, woodmice and squirrels. The spread of oak depends on the activities of these animals, for they lose many acorns after disturbing them; a bird that has eaten acorns may die or be killed miles away before it has begun to digest them, and such mischances also aid the dispersal of this large, heavy tree seed. Heavy crops of seed are only borne at intervals of a few years; these 'mast' years are usually followed by seasons of light fruiting, or by none at all.

If acorns are kept in cool moist surroundings they sprout readily in the spring after they fall. The nut itself and its two seed-leaves remain below ground, and the shoot that appears bears a few scale leaves, then normal foliage. The young root soon becomes a long stout tap root, and in the nursery the forester must transplant the seedling after the first season's growth to break this tap root and oblige the little tree to form the bushy side roots it needs for safe transplanting to the forest. Many oaks, however, spring up from 'bird-sown' acorns along hedgerows, on waste land or in woodland clearings. Oak is an aggressive tree which is always ready to establish itself as Britain's natural forest cover wherever fertile land is left ungrazed or unploughed.

Oak timber has always been prized for its great strength and handsome appearance, though special tools and techniques are needed to shape it. Each stem has a thin outer zone of sapwood which looks white on a newly felled tree, but is often stained dark, later on, by fungi feeding on its surface; this sapwood has no natural durability and rapidly decays unless treated with preservative. The heartwood within it is a rich golden brown colour and has remarkable natural durability, since it is impregnated with tannin. It will last without further treatment for hundreds of years in a roofed building, or for scores of years when exposed to damp as part of a fence or a ship. It has clear annual rings, well marked by the large pores of the springwood, and broad rays easily seen with the naked eye; when these rays are exposed by cleaving the trunk, they show as plates of 'silver grain', a lively decorative feature.

If iron is brought into contact with newly felled oak it reacts with the tannin in the wood to produce blue-black ink stains of the same composition as writing ink. You cannot drive an ordinary nail into oak anyway—it will bend first—so wooden pegs or brass screws are used where appearance matters. Oak can readily be sawn with saws designed for hardwoods, and it gives a good surface when cut by sharp planes or chisels. It is widely used for joinery and furniture of the high-class, permanent kind, such as is wanted in churches and public buildings, and also for coffins. Large, clean-grown oak trees, a hundred years old or more, fetch high prices for such purposes, while still larger sums are paid for very big trunks that can be sawn or sliced into decorative veneers. Oak is also the chosen wood for barrel staves, ladder rungs and wheel spokes.

Smaller, less valuable oak logs are cleft into sections for use as fence stakes, or hewn to a square outline to serve as gate-posts; sawn timber is used for fencing also, because of its natural durability. In the past the craft of hewing to shape was applied to oak on a much wider scale. The framework and roof timbers of old 'half-timbered' houses, and the roof timbers of old churches and barns, are always oak, and if you look at them closely you will see that they bear the marks of an axe or an adze; the saw was only used for cross-cutting. Likewise, all the oak used for the keels and ribs of wooden sailing ships—

Britain's 'hearts of oak' in time of war—was hewn to shape, only the deck planking being sawn. Oak is still used for the frames of wooden fishing craft built on the east coast of Scotland. It was formerly used for railway waggons, and it finds application in bridge-building, heavy engineering and dock work.

Oak branchwood has a ready sale as firewood logs; it also makes good charcoal. The bark was formerly harvested everywhere, wherever oak was felled, as a valuable source of tannin for turning hides into leather. It has now been supplanted by imported extracts from other trees, but a little is still harvested each spring, when it strips easily from the wood. Most of the poor scrub oakwoods of south-west England, Wales and western Scotland are abandoned coppices once worked for tanbark, firewood, fence stakes, pit props and charcoal wood. Nowadays landowners only plant oak on good lowland ground where it will reach the big sizes that fetch high prices; most planting is done in the south of England.

The name 'oak' has many local forms in different parts of Britain, from 'aik' in Scotland to 'woke' in Dorset and 'yuk' and 'yak' in Hampshire. Place-names including 'oak' are very common indeed; Ackworth, meaning oak farm, in Yorkshire, is an example. All these are related to its varied Teutonic names: *Eiche* in German; *eik* in Dutch; *ek* in Swedish; and *eg* in Danish and Norwegian. The acorn was originally 'aik corn', the grain of the oak. The Welsh name for oak is *derwen* —hence the River Derwent—while Gaelic and Irish names are *dair* and *darach;* all these are frequent in place names too. The French name is *chêne*, the form used in the Channel Islands being *quesne*.

All oaks belong to the genus *Quercus* which was their Roman name. The commonest species is the Pedunculate oak, *Quercus robur*, which has its female flowers and acorns on a *long stalk* or peduncle. These acorns are broadly oval with blunt tips, while the leaves are stalkless or almost so, and have two little lobes called auricles at their base. The Sessile oak,

*Q. petraea*, is so called because its female catkins and its tapering, conical acorns are *stalkless*, while each leaf has a distinct stalk. Sessile oak has the better timber form, since it keeps a main trunk growing up through its crown of branches. The two species interbreed, and many woods consist of hybrids or intermediate forms. Both kinds are found together, right across northern Europe, but as oaks need warmth they are valley trees amid the Alps and other high mountains. In the north oak only reaches to southern Norway, though it was the main timber used for the Viking ships, and in fact for all European wooden craft. The specific name *robur* is an alternative Roman word for oak tree, while *petraea* is derived from *petra*, a rock, in allusion to the tree's sturdiness.

Many other kinds of oaks are found in southern and eastern Europe, Asia and North America, but only a few are grown, on a small scale, in Britain. The Turkey oak, *Quercus cerris*, can be told by the long stipules on its winter buds, the saw-tooth-like lobes on its long leaves and the mossy green hairs on its acorn cups. The acorns take eighteen months to ripen. Once planted for ornament, Turkey oak has become naturalized in England, Wales and Ireland. Though the Turks value its timber, that grown in Britain is prone to warp and shrink, and few merchants will buy it. *Cerris* is an ancient name for oak. Buds are shown on page 47.

In 1765 a remarkable hybrid between Turkey oak and the Cork oak was discovered by an Exeter nurseryman named Lucombe. This Lucombe oak forms a magnificent park tree, with leaves like the Turkey oak but dark green above and also more or less evergreen; it is increased by grafting.

The Holm oak, *Quercus ilex* (Plate 95), is a striking evergreen tree like a large holly; in fact its English name means 'holly oak'; *ilex* was its Roman name. Its leaves, however, are never spiny like those of holly, and they are almost white, not green, below (p. 32). They are oval in shape and pointed, and may have a smooth or a toothed edge. The buds, as in other oaks, are clustered, and its fruit is a short round acorn, set in a typical cup. Self-sown seedlings are occasionally found. The bark is rough, dark black and rich in tannin; the wood is hard and tough. Holm oak comes from the Mediterranean lands and has been planted throughout the British Isles since the sixteenth century as an unusual decorative tree which gives good shelter; it casts a dense shade all the year round. It is absolutely resistant to salt sea winds; a splendid avenue of Holm oak thrives near the south coast at Goring in Sussex. Our biggest Holm oak, eighty-two feet tall and twenty feet round, stands at Knightshayes in Devon. The French name for the Holm oak is *yeuse*.

The Cork oak, *Q. suber* (*suber* means cork), which also grows around the Mediterranean, is another evergreen kind, but barely hardy in Britain. It may be known by its thick bark which is stripped in Spain to yield cork—rough 'virgin cork' from the first stripping, but finer stuff, suitable for bottle stoppers, at each subsequent harvest. Bark removal kills most trees, but in this one the bark breaks away at the bark cambium (see p. 6), leaving the tissues below unharmed.

Several kinds of American red oaks are grown for their bright foliage and vivid autumn colours. The commonest is the Northern red oak, *Quercus borealis* (*borealis* means northern), which bears leaves with sharply angled lobes. Its acorns, which are round and dumpy and sit on a flattish cup, take two years to ripen. It grows vigorously, but its wood lacks the strength and durability of the native oaks.

## Sweet Chestnut

*Castanea sativa*                                                    FAGACEAE

The earliest examples of the Sweet chestnut's charcoal and wood that have been found in Britain come from places where the Romans had forts and villas, so there can be little doubt that these people introduced this handsome and useful tree. It is native to the Mediterranean region, but has been cultivated for its nuts and timber throughout Europe. The Romans nourished their legions on its nuts, making a meal from them called *pollenta* which is still relished in Corsica today. The tree is easily raised from seed, and would be a first choice for an orchard in any Roman colony. All the names for this tree stem from the Roman *castanea*, including French *châtaignier*, German *Kastanie*, also *Edelkastanie*, or noble chestnut, Welsh *castanwydden*, and Scots 'chasten'. The English 'chestnut', formed by adding 'nut' to the Latin root, probably goes back to Saxon times, for there was a wood of chestnuts in the Forest of Dean in 1170. The specific name *sativa* means 'cultivated'.

Sweet chestnut is commonest in the south, where it ripens its nuts well in many seasons and often springs up from self-sown seed. North of the Midlands it is still hardy, but its nuts are rarely well filled, and it is grown only as a decorative tree. When it is in leaf, the remarkably large oval blades, often nine inches long, with their bold saw-tooth-like edges, mark it out; a vein runs out to each notch on the side of the leaf, and continues beyond it to form a short point. In winter the angular, strongly ribbed twigs, which bear roundish yet pointed reddish-brown buds, set alternately on little ledges, are equally distinctive (p. 46).

Sweet chestnut flowers later than most trees. In July it opens its catkins which are remarkable for having both male and female flowers on the same stalk (Plate 98), though often the female ones fail to develop. This arrangement aids insect pollination. Towards the tip of the stalk, which is about five inches long, there are many groups of male flowers, each group being spaced at intervals along it. Each group is made up of six bracts and seven flowers, while each flower consists of a six-lobed calyx, holding about ten stamens; but all you can see without dissection is a mass of green scale-leaves with golden anthers emerging from them. The pollen is mainly airborne, but insects also eat it and carry it, and are possibly attracted by the flowers' musty smell.

The female flower groups stand nearer the foot of the stalk, and each group is seen as a green, hairy, oval structure, from which a tuft of stigmas projects. It actually holds three flowers, each of which has a six-lobed calyx and a pistil with from three to six carpels or cells. Despite this complex structure, only one seed ripens in each flower. Each flower group develops rapidly

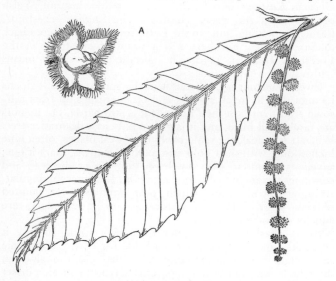

**Sweet Chestnut, in flower**
A, fruit, showing nuts and husk

during late summer into a green cupule clad in a mass of thin green spikes, ending in sharp points. This splits into four lobes when it is ripe, usually after it has fallen to the forest floor, and exposes up to three chestnuts that have developed within it, one from each little flower. Sometimes all three nuts have filled out, but more often only one or two have grown properly. Each is an oval, pointed nut with a hard shell; it bears at its tip a tuft of tiny hairs, the remains of the flower's stigmas.

Chestnuts are both nutritious and delicious, and are eaten in a pleasing variety of ways—roast, boiled or made into sweet-meats called marrons. This last word comes to us from France, where the tree is also called the *marronier*. As the home crop is so uncertain, nearly all of those we buy come from Italy or Spain, where fruiting varieties are carefully tended. Animals and birds relish them also, and only a few survive to produce new trees.

The seeds are not easy to store through the winter, but if they are kept in moist sand most of them will sprout next spring. The seed-leaves remain below ground, and normal leaves are borne from the outset. Seedlings grow so fast that they are usually sent out to the forest after a single season's growth.

Sweet chestnut forms a massive upright tree with bold branches (Plates 96, 97). Our tallest, at Cowdray Park in Sussex, is 114 feet high; the stoutest, at Canford in Dorset, is forty feet round. The bark is smooth and brown on young stems, but later it becomes a clear grey and eventually it develops deep fissures; the intervening ribs often show a spiral trend (Plate 99). The timber has a general resemblance to oak, and the heartwood is equally durable, but there are notable points of difference. In the Sweet chestnut the sap-wood zone is very narrow, and the rays are very small and invisible to the naked eye; as a big trunk seasons after felling, it often develops thin cracks called 'shakes' along the lines of the annual rings. All this means that chestnut rarely gives large sound planks, nor does it show silver grain; so despite its strength it is worth less than oak, and can only be used for lesser furniture, joinery and fencing. The wood is rich in tannin, and in Italy extracts are made from branchwood and sold for treating leather. It burns well, but is apt to spit out burning cinders, so it is better used for charcoal. Chestnut can also be used for hardwood paper pulp. Like oak, it gives ink stains where it touches iron.

Most of our chestnut woods today are coppices, for this is one of the few trees that are still profitable when so grown. The coppice crops are formed by planting seedlings and then cutting them back, so that their stumps send up groups of poles. These can be cut repeatedly, at intervals of twelve years or so, and each crop can well be worth £100 an acre today, which is a good return from poor land. The annual fall of golden-brown leaves proves a good fertilizer. Nearly all the poles are cleft by hand into triangular stakes for 'pale and wire' fencing, which is cheap, light and durable, owing to the heartwood found even in quite small pieces. Larger poles are used to support wires for training hops or as durable fence posts. Most of the coppices are in Kent, Sussex, Surrey and Hampshire, with a few in Herefordshire. In Scotland, northern England, Wales and Ireland the Sweet chestnut is seen only as a park tree. It does not need a rich soil, but it will not thrive on chalk or limestone.

# Beech

*Fagus sylvatica*                                        FAGACEAE

Beech is easily known by its long slender buds which are pale brown in colour and have papery scales (p. 51). They are set alternately on long, thin, zig-zag twigs, or else on short shoots which do not grow substantially longer. The leaves are a vivid pale green when they break forth in April, and later become a rich deep green shade; in autumn they fade to a rich golden-brown, colouring the forest floor where they lie in deep drifts. On young trees and beech hedges, however, they do not fall until spring, preserving a pleasing brown hue through winter and giving extra shelter. Each leaf has a short stalk and is oval in outline, ending in a short point. The edge is wavy and sometimes slightly toothed, and on newly opened leaves you may find a fringe of white hairs, which disappears later.

Beech always bears a dense crown of foliage which lets

little light through, so the floor of a beechwood supports few or no green plants, grasses or even moss. Young beech trees, however, can grow in quite dense shade, and though you will only find them on edges or clearings of a *beech* wood, they can thrive in the lighter shade cast by oak and other trees. This means that beech can often, by slow stages, replace oak as the 'climax' tree of natural forests. It is only in the south-east of England that this has happened in Britain, for the beech was a fairly late arrival, coming in about 2500 B.C. It spread naturally across the Midlands and into South Wales, and scattered prehistoric pollen grains—too few to establish the presence of anything more than occasional trees—have been found on the Scottish Borders and even in Ireland. Our most extensive beechwoods are on the chalk of the Chiltern Hills and the limestones of the Cotswolds; in both places natural regrowth is abundant and many of the woods hold both young and old trees.

The flowers of beech are wind-pollinated, and they open in May after the leaves are out; but you will not find them every year because beech only bears blossoms once in every two or three years, and heavy seed crops once in every four or five. The male catkins are borne in groups of two or three, a few inches back from the tips of the twigs. Each catkin has a long thin drooping stalk which bears two or three slender scale leaves and ends in a tassel of about fifteen small flowers. Each separate flower has a hairy, four-lobed, green calyx and about eight yellow stamens.

The female catkins, borne nearer the tips of the twigs, attract little notice, being small and green. Each catkin has a short, stout stalk, which ends in an oval cup, technically a cupule, from which there protrude the tips of two tiny flowers. If the cupule is opened you will see that each of the flowers has a four-lobed calyx and a pistil with three stigmas that sweep back in curves. Each flower yields a single seed, and the seeds develop together within the cupule.

This cupule ripens through the summer as an egg-shaped,

pointed object clad in stout yet soft green hairs (Plate 102).
In autumn the hairs turn brown and the husk splits into four
lobes, exposing within it one or two triangular, smooth,
shining brown seeds—the beech nuts. In a poor year, and in

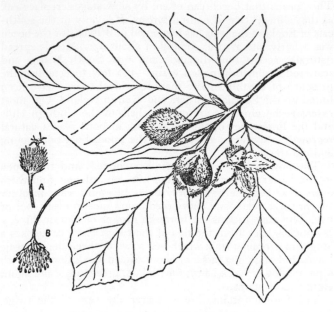

**Leaves, flowers, and fruits of Beech**
A, female flowers; B, male flowers

most districts north of the Midlands, a high proportion of the
nuts themselves will prove empty and useless. But in a good
'mast' year in the south, every nut will hold a firm, white,
nutritious kernel which is quite wholesome to eat.

The rain of nuts that falls to the forest floor is sure to

attract flocks of wood pigeons, besides pheasants, rooks, jays, squirrels, wood-mice, rabbits and in fact every kind of nut-eating bird and beast. In the New Forest and the Forest of Dean, pigs roaming the woods under the old custom of pannage root up many beech nuts, and sheep, horses and cattle also chew them. The spread of beech depends on chance carriage of nuts that are not destroyed in this way. In a good mast year many seedlings spring up in the shade of old trees, but most die out through lack of light later on.

Beech nuts sprout the spring after falling, and their first pair of seed-leaves is quite unlike the normal foliage which succeeds them, for they are broad, rounded, fat and fleshy and stand on a pinkish-white stalk. Beech is easily raised in cultivation, the seedlings being transplanted when one year old and grown on for a further year or two as transplants until they are big enough for the forest. Beech is planted on a large scale because it yields a good volume of useful readily marketed timber and is well suited to certain soils. It is perfectly at home on chalk downs and limestone hills, where few other trees reach timber size. Its early growth in the woods is helped by shelter from strong winds, hot sun, and late spring frosts, and therefore it is often planted with a conifer 'nurse', or under the shelter of light birch cover. Later it becomes a hardy and wind-firm tree, and will, for example, flourish 1,200 feet above sea level in the exposed Peak District, where it is used for shelter belts on the limestone. On the sea coast, however, its leaves suffer severely from salt-scorch. As a park tree, it has been planted on every large estate in Britain and Ireland, and on good lowland ground it thrives even in the far north of Scotland, producing magnificent crowns and trunks of great size and high timber value. Our tallest beech, 142 feet high, is at Yester House, East Lothian, Scotland, and our stoutest, twenty-six feet round, is at Eridge Park in Sussex.

Beech bark is a typical bright metallic grey colour, and it remains smooth even when the tree ages. The base of a large trunk is nearly always buttressed (Plate 104). The crown breaks up into a spreading network of fine branches (Plates 100, 101). Beech timber is easily known by its bright buff colour, and by the presence of little chocolate-brown specks all through it; these are actually the rays, exposed in various shapes on all surfaces no matter how the wood is cut. The heartwood is the same shade as the sapwood, and has no natural durability, so beech is rarely used out of doors. Beech is a first-rate firewood.

The big commercial demand for beech is due to its strength, its availability in quantity and large sizes, and the ease with which it can be worked to a good finish in any direction of the grain. It is a leading furniture timber, and is also used for a multitude of purposes where a hard, strong, stable piece of wood is required. Examples are flooring blocks, mallet heads and plane stocks. Being a good turnery timber, it is used for handles, bowls and wooden porridge spoons. Other applications are in joinery, shopfitting and the manufacture of plywood, and also for hardwood paper pulp.

Beech grows wild over most of northern Europe. Its range includes all Denmark, where it is the national tree, and southern Sweden; but it only just reaches Norway. In the Alps and other high mountain ranges the beechwoods flourish on the lower foothills, giving way to silver fir and spruce higher up. The Copper beech, variety *purpurea*, is a natural 'sport' that was discovered in Thuringia, Germany, in the eighteenth century. It is usually grafted but will also grow from seed. The rich purplish-brown colour of its leaves masks their green chlorophyll below, and they function normally.

Our name 'beech', from Anglo-Saxon *beoce*, is clearly related to German *Buche*, Dutch *beuk*, Danish and Norwegian *bøg* and *bøk*, and Swedish *bok*. Beech is a common element in English place-names, both old and new; sometimes, as at Long Buckby, meaning beech village, it survives in its Danish form. The English word 'book' is derived from the rune-books of the Norsemen, so called because they carved their letters on flat pieces of beech or rowan wood. The German word for book, *Buch*, is likewise linked to the beech tree, and so is its Danish equivalent, *bog*.

The scientific name, *Fagus sylvatica*, means 'beech tree of the woods' and the Roman name of *fagus* resembles Welsh *ffawydden*, Irish *feaġa* and Gaelic *faibhle*. The French name is *hêtre*.

# Willows

*Salix* species                                    SALICACEAE

Willows show many patterns of growth, form and leaf, but all can be identified as *willows* by a simple feature of their buds. These are nearly always alternate and are always enclosed by a single bud-scale (p. 46); the only bud remotely like this is that of the plane (p. 45), but that is conical and encircled by a leaf-scar. All willows have simple leaves without lobes, but the shape varies with the species; a representative selection is shown in Plate 112. In nature the male flowers are, almost invariably, borne on separate trees from the female ones, but I once found a weeping willow bearing flowers of both sexes, the female flowers being on drooping branches, and the male flowers on abnormal ones that grew upwards.

Most willows flower before their leaves open, that is, in March; but some delay flowering until May, after the leaves are out. Pollination is partly by insects, and willow catkins are eagerly sought by the bees in early spring. Conventional botany books always describe willows as 'insect-pollinated', but recent experiments have shown that, as one would expect from the structure of the catkins, much pollen is airborne and can be caught in 'pollen traps'; wind is probably the major agent of pollination. All willow flowers are very simple, lacking petals, but the catkins are showy because of their massed golden anthers or silvery-haired pistils, and insects find them easily. In a male catkin there are a large number of very simple flowers, each consisting of a bract carrying many silky hairs, a nectary and from two to twelve stamens ending in bright yellow anthers. The female catkin (Plate 107) consists of many small flowers, each of which has a bract clad in hairs, a nectary and a flask-shaped pistil topped by two stigmas. In both sexes the catkins are oval and downy, but the yellow colour marks out the male.

After pollination the pistils ripen rapidly into green bottle-shaped structures, which split as soon as ripe, from June, in some kinds, to October or even later, in others. They release a number of exceedingly small seeds, each with a tuft of white hairs, so plentifully that a seed-bearing willow appears covered with white down. The hairs support the minute seed on the air, and it can be carried on the winds over great distances, often a matter of miles. Unless the seed alights on moist bare earth, with most species it has no hope of growth, and it will only sprout if it finds such a spot within a few days of its release; but in late-flowering kinds the seed sprouts next spring. In cultivation the seed of most common willows must be sown at once; it cannot be stored. You will only find these willows growing wild in places where moist bare earth is occasionally available at midsummer, particularly stream-sides and shingle banks, but occasionally on rubbish heaps, sand dunes, heaths or the fringes of woods where trees have shaded out the grass. Once established, willows can be trans-planted to any reasonable situation. They cannot, however, grow in soil waterlogged with stagnant moisture; the water must be moving and so carrying oxygen. Along streamsides they often develop most peculiar roots—pinkish-white net-works that trail in the stream and gather mineral nutrients as well as water.

Nearly all willows grow very readily from cuttings. Any piece of twig or branch, stuck upright in moist soil, will take root and send out shoots. A willow uprooted by floods is more than likely to take root again if it is stranded on a mudbank. Growers rarely raise willows from seed; instead they strike cuttings and so preserve the same 'clone' (p. 11). Each clone is either male or female. Willows do not send up sucker shoots from their roots, but any stem of a trailing willow which touches the ground may take root there. If cut back, willows send forth coppice shoots with amazing vigour (Plate 113). This method of growth is used commercially for the production of willow rods for basketry, which are one-year-old coppice shoots. If pollarded, that is, lopped at six feet above ground level, they send out a head of branches like the hair of a golliwog (p. 11). Along river banks in the Midlands farmers still tend pollard willows in this way, cutting the poles every few years for hurdle wood, fence repairs or rough basketry. Few willows show good tree form; most develop irregular branching crowns, as shown in Plate 110. They are not long-lived trees, nor do they ever grow very large.

Willow bark is smooth at first and in some varieties shows brilliant and attractive colours; willows with purple, red, orange or yellow bark are grown in gardens for winter colour, but in other sorts it is grey or brown. On older stems it becomes rough, with a characteristic diagonal network of ribs (Plate 106), remaining grey or brown. Willow wood is pale cream to pinkish-brown in colour. It shows no distinct heartwood but may be darker towards the tree's centre. It is made up of thin-walled cells, and although it is heavy when freshly felled and full of sap, once it is dry it is lighter than any other native timber. If kept dry, it is strong and supple, but out of doors it has no natural durability. It makes poor firewood, not burning at all when green, but burning away fast when seasoned. Branchwood, which has all the properties described, is widely used for baskets, hurdles, and screens. Stemwood is used only for cricket bats and a few other specialized purposes. Willow trees are grown for these uses, but not otherwise as timber crops. They always need full sunlight and are more often seen as solitary trees than in plantations.

All the features described above relate to the willows as a group. There are so many species, varieties and hybrids found growing wild, and so many cultivars grown in gardens and willow beds, that only a specialist can hope to name them all. Here we can describe only the more common and easily recognized kinds that grow, or can grow in tree form.

But before we turn to the trees, let us take a brief look at the dwarf shrub willows and those that trail over the ground. The commonest is the Creeping willow, *Salix repens*, which will be found on many damp heaths; its catkins peep up above the heather from a smooth orange stem that roots down at intervals. On sand dunes you will find the Sand willow, its variety *arenaria*, which helps to bind together the drifting sand. And near the summits of our highest mountains you will find arctic-alpine kinds like the bushy Woolly willow, *S. lanata*, which flourishes on damp screes that are under snowdrifts for much of the year. This and allied mountain willows are survivors of the first tundra vegetation that crept over Britain when the Ice Age ended about 15,000 B.C. Later came the taller shrub willows, and finally the tree willows. This explains why our willow flora varies from one district to another. Some of the taller kinds have hardly spread, except in cultivation, beyond the lowlands of the south and east; but there, of course, the arctic-alpine kinds have died out, though their remains persist in prehistoric peat deposits.

The names of willows are as confusing as their species. Most of those you see in print are 'academic' names invented by botanists and used by nobody else. A few are 'cultivar' names invented by nurserymen or the growers of basket willows. Other, truly 'common' names reflect only local custom and do not help you to tell one species from another, though they have an interesting history. Our usual name 'willow' comes from Anglo-Saxon *welig*, related to Dutch *wilg*, and meaning a pliant or 'willing' stem. 'Withy', another common term, has links with German *Weide*, Danish *vidie*, Norwegian *vier* and *vidje*, and Swedish *vide;* it comes from Old Norse *vithir* which is also the source of *withe*, a green stem for binding bundles. The Roman name, *salix*, is linked to French *saule*, Welsh *helygen* (wherein 'h' has replaced 's'), Gaelic *seileach* and Irish *saileaċ*. Related names are Scots 'saugh' and English 'sallow' or 'sally', German *Salweide*, Danish and Norwegian *selje* and Swedish *salg*. Other Scandinavian names are *pil* and *ris*.

'Osier', used mainly for basket willows, comes from French *osière* and Latin *ausaria*, meaning a willow bed. 'Pussy' willow refers to the soft down of the catkins, and 'palm' to their use as church decorations on Palm Sunday. As the English names vary so much, all kinds are called 'willow' here, except for two osiers.

The willow features in poetry and literature as the symbol of sorrow. Its bark is rich in tannin, but is not now used commercially; it also contains salicylic acid, a drug allied to aspirin. Charcoal from willow twigs is favoured by artists because it is less brittle than that made from other woods.

## White Willow

This tall handsome tree is easily known by its long narrow lance-shaped leaves (Plate 112), often five times as long as broad. Their colour on both sides is a gleaming silvery green, a feature found on no other tree; this effect is due to a coating of fine silky white hairs which mask the green colour beneath. It makes a mature White willow a magnificent sight, particularly when its foliage is stirred by the wind and its broad spreading crown reflects the passing sun (Plate 105). Our tallest specimen, at Grovelands Park in North London, is eighty-one feet high and eleven feet round. Though big enough to yield timber, the White willow is usually grown as a pollard tree, along river banks, for branchwood. Some strains of it are coppiced as basket willows. It is commonest in the south, but can be found in the lowlands anywhere in the British Isles, and over most of Europe.

In winter the White willow can be distinguished from most other kinds by its thin, greyish-green twigs which are not brittle at the base. Its botanical name, *Salix alba*, means 'white willow', and it is so-called in every language. Its variety *vitellina*, the Golden willow, is grown as an ornamental shrub for its bright yellow twigs, to give winter colour.

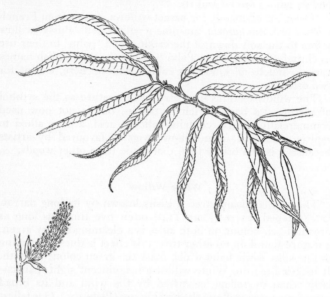

**White Willow, with male catkin**

### Cricket-bat Willow

Only one kind of willow is used for good cricket bats; this is a variety, *coerulea*, of the White willow. The name *coerulea* means 'blue' and the Cricket-bat willow is easily told by its bluish-green, not silvery green leaves, which are less hairy than those of the White willow, though similar in shape. It has a beautiful pyramidal crown, and merits growing as an ornamental tree. You will find it very commonly in Essex and Suffolk, where most bat timber is grown, less frequently in neighbouring south-eastern counties, and only occasionally elsewhere. The variety arose naturally in the south-east, and is increased solely by cuttings; most trees belong to a female clone, though a male form exists. Outside England it does not occur naturally, nor is it commonly planted.

For bat production the young willows must be planted on good farm land which is beside a stream or otherwise well watered. Sets, that is, stout cuttings, six feet high, are planted thirty feet apart; as they grow, their lower side branches are pruned off to stop big knots forming. After twelve years or so the willows are around forty feet high and five feet round (Plate 106). They are then sold to bat makers who fell them for their valuable lower stems. The lowest eight feet of the trunk is cleft by hand—never sawn—into triangular segments, each of which is then cross-cut to give three bat 'clefts'. About twenty-four bats can be made from one tree. The clefts are carefully seasoned and then shaped by hand. Fast-grown willow is preferred for bats because it is very light yet very tough, and does not warp after proper cleaving, seasoning and shaping. The same material is used for making artificial limbs, again because it is light and tough.

### Crack Willow

This peculiar tree is common along streamsides, where it is sometimes grown, or at least treated as a pollard for its branchwood. Its leaves (Plates 107, 112) are very like those of the White willow, but not quite so slender; they are a true green, not silvery in colour. But at any time of the year you can tell it by an odd feature: bend back any small twig and it will at once break off with a sharp 'crack' without any real force being used. This surprisingly brittle character extends to quite large branch junctions, though not to stout woody stems, and the wood is considered less strong than that of other willows. Where each twig breaks a neat circular scar is left, as though the tissues were designed for such an injury. It is actually a device for natural reproduction, since broken twigs have a fair chance of striking root on damp ground or stream banks.

Crack willow can form a tree of moderate size (Plate 110), up to fifty feet tall and five feet round, but breakages often

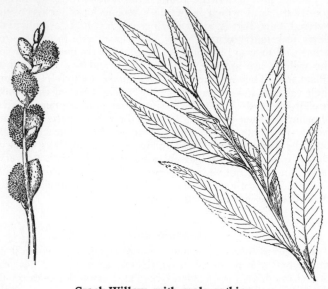

**Crack Willow, with male catkins**

make it form a straggling bush. Its twigs are orange-yellow in colour, with a smooth shining surface, and they bear slender, pointed, yellow buds. The flowers (Plate 107) are of the typical willow pattern. It is found throughout the British Isles and over most of Europe. The Latin name, *Salix fragilis*, means 'fragile willow', and all its other names are based on this feature. In Wales it is *helygen frau*, the brittle willow, in

German *Knackweide*, crack willow, and in Scandinavia *skorpil* or *braekkelig pil*, brittle or breaking willow.

## Weeping Willow

Beautiful cascades of weeping foliage make this tree easily known at sight, and even in winter the long, slender, yellow twigs mark it out. It was originally a native of China—it appears on the 'willow-pattern' plates—but it has been spread throughout the temperate regions as a cultivated, decorative tree (Plate 108). Its leaves are a striking bright pale green when they open in early March, before those of any other tree. They expand to become narrow lance-shaped blades, more slender than those of other willows. They are deep green above, bluish-green below, and they persist longer on the branches than the leaves of other trees.

Most Weeping willows are female, but occasionally a few male flowers appear on a 'female' tree. Many other weeping trees are really drooping branches which have to be grafted on to a tall upright stock; but this willow always weeps, and comes true from cuttings which are easy to root. There are, however, other weeping strains of willows, which need grafting.

The Weeping willow has rightly become a popular garden tree, but it is a little difficult to restrain in size without skilful pruning; left to itself it may grow fifty feet tall, with a trunk ten feet round. Its Latin name is *Salix babylonica*, in allusion to the passage in Psalm 137: 'By the rivers of Babylon, there we sat down, yea, we wept, when we remembered Zion. We hanged our harps upon the willows in the midst thereof'. It is uncertain, however, which willow was flourishing beside the Euphrates in those far-off days, though the first tree grown in Britain was brought from that region, about 1730, by a merchant named Vernon. All the common names for this tree mean 'weeping willow'. It is the *saule pleureur* of the French and the *Trauerweide* of the Germans.

## Almond-leaved Willow

This willow, a streamside tree of spreading habit and moderate size (Plate 111), shows a curious resemblance to the almond (p. 95). Its leaves have a similar long-oval shape, with toothed edges and a drawn-out tip (Plate 112); they have also a dark green and shining surface. All the green tissues have a scent recalling that of sweet almonds, too. The bark is not fissured like that of other willows, but breaks away in large reddish-brown flakes. Almond-leaved willow bears conspicuous flowers in April, when the golden-anthered male blossoms contrast effectively with the newly opened foliage; sometimes it flowers again in July or August. The Latin name, *Salix triandra*, is based on the peculiar feature that the male flower bears three stamens. This willow is commonest in south-east England, but can be found as far north as eastern Scotland, also in Ireland.

## Bay-leaved Willow

The Bay-leaved willow has a slight resemblance to the Sweet bay tree (p. 134), though it is not an evergreen. Its leaves (Plate 112) are similar in shape to those of Sweet bay, and have a similar shining dark green upper surface, together with a paler green lower one. They have a peculiar fragrance, but not the strong aromatic scent of the bay. Their edges are very finely toothed and bear little glands which exude a sticky substance. The twigs and buds are a glossy olive-brown like those of bay, but the leaf-stalks, which bear glands, are green, not red. As a rule this willow is seen as a bush, but it sometimes makes a tree fifty feet high, with greyish bark.

The Bay-leaved willow grows wild in Scotland, northern England, northern Ireland and North Wales, where it is often found beside becks and burns in dales and glens. Further south it is grown as a decorative shrub. It is found wild across the European continent, where it is mainly a northern tree, with a range from North Germany to Norway. Its German name is *Lorbeerweide*, laurel-willow, and its Norwegian one is *istervier*.

Bay-leaved willow flowers late, in May or June, and its flowers then make a pleasing contrast to its foliage. The male catkins, being balls of golden anthers, are very showy. The flowers have a pleasant fragrance, which helps to attract insects. In the male flower there are five stamens, a useful feature for identification, and the source of the tree's Latin name, *Salix pentandra*. The seed capsules open very late, and the female trees then attract attention since the massed seed-hairs look like strings of woolly down. Seed dispersal is not complete until winter, and many seedlings apparently do not sprout until next spring; this may be an adaptation to the short summers of northern lands.

### Goat Willow

The name of this tree puzzles many people, especially as it is repeated by its Latin name, *Salix caprea*; but its leaves are a favourite food of browsing goats, and were valued as fodder because they open early in spring when grass is scarce. Pale green at first, they soon expand into a broadly oval shape, with a wrinkled surface, a toothed edge and a short blunt tip (Plate 112); they have two prominent stipules—little leaflets—at the base of the stalk. The twigs are smooth and reddish brown, and the winter buds are large and round. The bark of the branches is greenish-brown, that of older trunks dark brown but still smooth. Goat willow is usually seen as a straggling bush on the edge of ponds; occasionally it forms a small tree thirty feet high.

Goat willow catkins open early in March, well before the leaves, and so they are widely gathered as decorative 'palm' or 'pussy willow'. The golden-anthered males are showy, but the silvery downy female ones are attractive too, and last longer. Most bushes recover remarkably well from this annual flower-plucking. The Goat willow, also called the Great sallow, has a wide distribution over the British Isles, and is a common shrub all over Europe. In Germany it is called *Salweide* or *Palmweide*, and in France *marsault*.

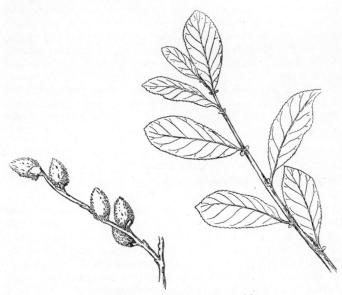

**Goat Willow, with female catkins**

### Common Osier

Many kinds of willows can be grown to produce rods for basketry by first planting cuttings and then, once they are well established, cutting them back annually so that they send up a cluster of coppice shoots. But most of those grown commercially are varieties of the Common osier, *Salix viminalis*, which has been selected because of its long, supple twigs. It is easily recognized by its exceptionally long and narrow leaves, many times longer than broad; they have a soft texture and a margin which is rolled back and bears no teeth. Pale green above, they are clad below in silvery silky down, which makes an osier bed resemble a gleaming white cloud when the wind stirs the willows on a sunny day. The twigs are downy towards the tip but smooth at the base, and the buds are long and narrow. The Common osier is a native tree; though it is uncommon in the wild it is cultivated on all the British Islands, including Orkney and Shetland. Left to itself it develops a woody stem and grows up to thirty feet tall.

In cultivation it has usually the form illustrated for Purple osier in Plate 113, a cluster of stems springing from a single rootstock, but with much finer stems. Formerly osier beds were found in many districts, but today the only region where their tending is important commercially is the Isle of Athelney in Somerset, where they are grown on very fertile land reclaimed from the fens and drained by ditches. The beds are established by planting cuttings only two feet apart. At each annual cutting, done in the autumn, the rods, as they are called, are bound in large bundles for transport. Some, called brown willow rods, are sold with their bark still on for rough baskets needing extra strength; others have the bark peeled off by simple machinery to give white rods; and others again are first boiled in their bark and then peeled, because the bark holds a natural dye which produces the striking buff shade favoured for many baskets.

Most rods are used in the round, but some are cleft. They are stored dry, but the basket-maker has to moisten them again before he can work them. They then become supple, but after weaving they 'set' in their new shape and become firm once more. This property, together with their considerable strength for such light weight and a natural springiness that protects the goods being carried, ensures the use of hand-woven baskets in a multitude of shapes and sizes for carrying all kinds of goods.

Small osier beds are found here and there in valleys running down to the sea; their rods are woven locally into lobster-pots, crab-traps, and coarse baskets.

**Common Osier, with male catkins**

### Other Willows

A common and widely spread shrub very similar to the Goat willow is the Grey willow, *Salix cinerea*, also called the Common sallow. This can generally be known by the shape of its leaves, which are obovate, that is, oval but becoming wider towards the tip, then suddenly narrowing. The lower surface of these leaves is densely clad in grey hairs, while the upper surface is also greyish-green.

The Eared willow, *Salix aurita*, also called the Wrinkled sallow, is easily known because at the base of each leaf-stalk there are two 'ears', which are well-developed leafy stipules. Its leaves, which are broadly oval and have deeply toothed edges, have a wrinkled surface due to their deeply set veins. This species too is found on all the British Islands, including the Orkneys and Shetlands.

The Tea-leaved willow, *Salix phylicifolia*, is so-called because its leaves resemble those of the tea bush. They are small, smooth, oval and neat, glossy dark green above and blue-green below, and have no obvious hairy covering or stipules. The twigs are quite smooth and of a glossy chestnut colour. Allied to it, but distinguished by downy twigs and leaves, is the Dark-leaved willow, *S. nigricans*, so-called because its leaves turn black when they are dried for the herbarium. These are both northern species found only in Scotland, the north of England and the north of Ireland. They flower late, in May after the leaves are out, and ripen seed in September; apparently the seed does not sprout until the following spring. It is known that many 'perishable' seeds retain their germinative power for months at low temperatures, around freezing point, and it may be that farther south the winters are too warm to suit the seeding habit of these willows.

The Violet willow, *Salix daphnoides*, a native of central Europe, is often planted in gardens for the beauty of its winter twigs, which are rich purple in colour and covered with a glistening white waxy bloom. Its catkins, which open before the leaves, are remarkably showy and have a furry texture. Its leaves are lance-shaped, and the bark on old stems is smooth and green; it may form a tree forty feet in height.

Finally the Purple osier, *Salix purpurea*, differs from all other willows in bearing its leaves in pairs, almost, if not quite, opposite each other (p. 41). Despite its name, its twigs are scarlet or buff, not purple, for the word *purpurea* is here used in its old Roman sense of bright red. It bears narrow buds,

narrow lance-shaped leaves like those of the common osier, but
bluish-green beneath, and showy catkins which open before the
leaves; the male ones have brick-red anthers, but shed yellow
pollen. It is grown for basketry, as well as a decorative shrub
(Plate 113). The Purple osier is native, and has a general distribution over Britain and Ireland.

**Purple Osier**
The only willow with paired leaves and buds

# Poplars

*Populus* species                                    SALICACEAE

The main feature that enables everyone to tell a poplar at sight is the incessant trembling motion of its leaves under the least breath of air. This quivering takes place because the leaf stalk, which is long and slender, is not round but flattened from side to side so that the leaf blade has no stability and wobbles very easily. The word 'poplar' comes from Roman *populus*, which arises in turn from the Greek word *papaillo*, meaning to shake; a related word with the same idea is *papillon*, the French for butterfly. Most names for poplar come from the Latin, including French *peuplier*, Welsh *poplysen*, German *Pappel*, Dutch *populier*, and Danish *poppel*. But in America poplars are often called cottonwoods because of their downy seeds. Poplar leaves are always simple, but their shape varies from triangular to oval, elliptic or rhombic, and sometimes they are lobed (p. 207). Whatever their shape, a curious feature marks them out from the leaves of all other trees—their veins are *random*, wandering over the leaf blade without a set plan, and without the neat balance between the two sides of the main vein, which one finds with other trees.

In winter you can pick out poplars by their vigorous branching habit, and as a rule a lack of symmetry in the crown (Plates 116, 119); often a tree looks like a 'branch stuck in the ground'. This one-sidedness arises from the irregular placement of the buds: these are never paired, neither are they neatly alternate; instead they are set at uneven intervals on *all* sides of the twigs. The twigs often bear strong ridges below the buds, which show several surface scales and are oval and pointed (p. 50). In some kinds they are sticky and pleasantly fragrant.

Poplar bark, smooth at first, becomes remarkably thick and rugged on old trees (Plates 117, 120); its colour varies with the species. Poplar wood is unlike that of any other tree. It is white in colour, or nearly so, and is very open in texture. When freshly felled, it is full of water and therefore very heavy, and in that state it will not burn. But when it is fully seasoned and all the water has evaporated, it becomes extremely light, and then burns too fast to be of any real use for firewood or charcoal. Nevertheless it is always preferred for matches; this is partly because its open texture is ideal for holding paraffin wax, the real fuel in a match stick. The other reason is that its 'woolly' fibres do not readily split, and so a thin match can be struck without breaking or splintering. This same power of holding together in thin sections ensures its use for the veneers from which match boxes are made, and also the white, light, cheap and clean 'chip' baskets used for marketing fruit and watercress. The matches themselves are cut from thicker veneers of poplar wood.

Good stout poplar logs, which have had their lower side branches pruned off years ago to prevent knots forming, fetch attractive prices as veneer logs. Otherwise poplar timber has no special uses, though the branchwood and waste make good paper pulp. The heartwood is sometimes distinguished by a brown, pinkish, or even a purplish tinge; it has no natural durability.

Poplars always bear male and female catkins on separate trees. Their flowers open in March before the leaves, and are always wind-pollinated. The male catkins are shaped like lambs' tails and are often conspicuous because of the red colour of their massed anthers, which shed golden pollen (Plate 115). On examination each catkin is seen to have a long stalk, bearing very numerous, very simple flowers. Each separate flower consists of a large bract, which has a wavy edge and bears a shaggy coat of hairs, and a stalk carrying a little cup, on which sit about ten stamens, with large red or purple anthers. The catkin as a whole resembles a fat, hairy, pinkish caterpillar.

The female catkins attract less notice at first because they are more slender and greener in colour. Each separate flower has a hairy bract, and a short-stalked cup which bears a flask-shaped green pistil, topped by three stigmas. After pollination the female catkins grow larger quite rapidly and ripen their fruits by midsummer. Each fruit catkin is then seen as a long stalk, bearing on shorter stalks the oval fruits of the separate flowers, so that the whole structure looks like a green necklace (Plate 121). Each fruit is a capsule or little box holding many very tiny seeds, and each seed bears a tuft of hairs which enable it to remain airborne for long periods. When the capsules open a cloud of downy seed emerges and drifts everywhere. Female poplars are therefore disliked by gardeners who have to keep paths tidy, and still more so by house-painters. Nurserymen who raise ornamental trees seldom stock them, and in consequence they are quite rare trees.

Poplar seeds only grow if they land on moist earth within a few days of release. Germination is very rapid indeed, occurring within two or three days. Two tiny, oval, fleshy seed-leaves, indented at the base, appear first; normal foliage follows and growth is remarkably fast. In practice poplars are only raised from seed when foresters wish to breed new hybrid kinds. Nearly all poplars strike with great readiness from branch cuttings; the few exceptions are increased by sucker shoots cut away from the roots of the parent trees. In these ways growers always propagate a known 'clone' with characters just like that of its parent tree.

During the summer poplars transpire water very rapidly, and therefore they grow best on well-watered ground such as fertile fens with moving moisture, close to rivers. This thirstiness can cause problems if they are planted near build-ings on heavy clay soils in districts of low rainfall, for they intensify the drying-out of the clay, and its movement and cracking may endanger foundations. Poplars always need full light, and will not grow in the shade of other trees.

Many species and varieties of poplars grow in all parts of the North temperate zone, and as cross-breeding is easy, many hybrids have been developed. The number of known named clones in cultivation runs into hundreds, and few botanists

claim to recognize them all; those required for timber production are in fact often sold on certificates of origin. Here we
can only describe three native kinds and a few of the more
conspicuous introductions and hybrids commonly grown.

### Aspen

The aspen is an undoubted native all over the British Isles,
growing wild even in the Shetlands. It is one of the world's
most northerly trees, and it thrives in Scandinavia right to the
Arctic circle. In Switzerland it springs up on the fringes of
Alpine glaciers, helping to fix moraines and check avalanches.
In such places it is no more than a bushy shrub, which renews
itself when damaged by sending up a thicket of sucker shoots
from its roots. Its seedlings are well adapted to colonize fresh
bare earth exposed by erosion, since they strike root in the
few weeks after midsummer when the soil is warm and frost-
free. In the lowlands aspen becomes a much larger tree, though
it retains its suckering habit. Aspens of good form are prized
above all other poplars for match making in Scandinavia. By
crossing the European race, *Populus tremula*, with the American
Bigtooth aspen, *P. tremuloides*, the Swedes have produced the
hybrid Giant Aspen, which grows quickly to greater size than
others; it is increased, like the common kind, by root cuttings.

Aspen reached Britain very early, about 10,000 B.C. Nowadays it is most often found as an upland riverside tree, and
its roots bind shingle banks together and help to check erosion.
It also grows beside streams and ponds in odd places in the
southern lowlands. With us it seldom reaches timber size so it
is never planted for its wood. You can easily tell it by the
round leaves on normal branches. These have a pretty indented edge and stand on long, thin, flattened leaf stalks that
allow them to quiver in the wind to an even greater degree
than other poplar leaves. On sucker shoots, however, the
leaves are heart-shaped with a pointed tip and are larger than
normal. All the leaves are mid-green in summer, but change in

autumn to striking shades of gold, red and purple. The male catkins are very woolly (Plate 115), with purple anthers contrasting with yellow pollen, while the female ones are green. The bark is smooth and pale grey on young stems, becoming rough and dark grey on old trunks.

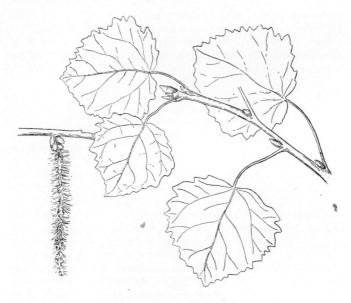

**Aspen, with male catkin**

*Tremula* is the Roman name for this tree, and the source of its French name *tremble;* it means, of course, to tremble or shake. 'Aspen' is an old Teutonic name, represented by *aespe* or *aepse* in Anglo-Saxon, *Aspe* in German, *asp* or *baevreaspe* in Danish and Swedish, and *osp* in Norwegian. Place-names based on it include Espley in Northumberland,

Apsley in Warwickshire, and Ospisdale, meaning aspen valley, in Sutherland where this tree still flourishes. German *Zitter-pappel* and the Dutch *ratelpopulier* and *trilpopulier* all mean 'quaking poplar'.

The Gaelic name is *crann critheach*, the quivering tree, and this gives us Killiecrankie, wood of the aspens, in Perthshire, where aspens still abound. Irish names are *criteac̊* and *eada*. In Wales the aspen's proper name is *aethnen*, but the incessant motion of its leaves give rise to two colloquial names, *coed tafod merched* and *coed tafod gwragedd*, both meaning 'the tree of the woman's tongue'.

### Grey Poplar

In Britain the Grey poplar makes a much finer tree than the aspen, forming a shapely bole with an attractive white bark which only slowly becomes black and rugged at the base. The male flowers are crimson-coloured. The names of this tree arise from the fact that neither its stem nor its leaves are as white as those of the White poplar (see p. 207); its Latin name, *Populus canescens*, signifies 'grey', as do the French *peuplier gris* or *grisard*, German *Graupappel*, and Scandinavian *gråpoppel*. Some botanists regard it as an inter-mediate form, or hybrid, between aspen and White poplar. The supposed 'specific' difference between the White and the Grey poplars is that the leaves of the latter are never truly lobed. Actually they vary a great deal in shape, being oval on the twigs of mature trees but deeply indented on vigorous sucker shoots, and the text-book difference is of little value in the field. Probably the Grey poplar is the north-western race of the White one. For buds, see page 49.

The Grey poplar is native over the south and east of England, and commonly planted elsewhere. Good trunks make fair veneer timber, but it is rarely planted for its wood. Instead it is grown for ornament, or as shelter on the sea coast, where it

resists sea gales. Because of its suckering habit it helps to
stabilize landslips, such as occur on clay cliffs. Our tallest,
110 feet, is at Saling Grove in Essex, and our stoutest, eighteen
feet round, is at Castle Hedingham in the same county.

### White Poplar

The White poplar is a remarkably attractive tree, for the
lower sides of its leaves are clad in white down which gives a
silvery aspect to its foliage whenever it is stirred by the wind

**White Poplar**

(Plate 116); the upper surface of the leaves is smooth and mid-
green. Its bark is even whiter than that of Grey poplar, though
it shows a greenish tinge and eventually loses its smoothness
and becomes black and rugged near the tree foot (Plate 117).
The leaves show a marked variation with the vigour of the

shoot, being clearly five-lobed on suckers and strong leading shoots, but oval on slow-growing twigs. The male flowers are crimson. Buds are shown on page 49.

The White poplar is native to Europe and its natural range may possibly include the south-east of England. It was growing here in 1548, and there is no record of its earlier introduction. It is nowadays planted only as a decorative tree or for seaside shelter. Our largest recorded tree, eighty feet tall and seventeen feet round, is at Bayfordbury in Hertfordshire. All its names signify white or silvery, being *Populus alba* in Latin, *peuplier blanc* in French, *Silberpappel* in German and *sølvpoppel* in Danish. An old English name is 'abele', derived from Latin *alba*, white.

### Black Poplar

The Black poplar is only so-called to distinguish it from the White and the Grey ones. Its only really dark feature is its rugged bark, but it lacks the whiteness of leaf found on the other two. Nowadays it is a rather local tree, having been replaced for timber production by the hybrid kinds described later, since they grow faster. It can be distinguished from its hybrids by the presence of swellings on its trunk. It is native to the eastern counties and the Midlands of England, reaching as far north as Lancashire, and as far west as the Welsh Marches. John Evelyn recorded stately poplars growing in Cheshire in 1662, and in 1930 I saw some of their descendants, which were well over 120 feet tall and twenty feet round. Records are held by a tree 140 feet tall at Fairlawne in Kent, and one twenty-seven feet round at Shalford in Surrey. The leaves of the Black poplar are triangular to rhombic in shape, though the basal angles are rounded, not sharp. The tip has a blunt point, and the edge bears shallow teeth. They are mid-green in colour with translucent margins, and their long stalks are flattened close to the leaf-blade.

Most names for this tree mean simply 'Black poplar': in

Latin it is *Populus nigra*, in French *peuplier noir*, in German *Schwarzpappel*, in Dutch *zwarte populier* and in Danish *sortpoppel*. It is widely grown as a street and park tree in the industrial north of England, but its name of 'Manchester poplar' arises from the fact that it is native to that district, besides enduring the city's smoke.

**Black Poplar**

### Lombardy Poplar

The plume-like outline of this graceful poplar, well shown in Plates 122 and 123, mark it out from all other common trees. It is caused by all the side branches following the upward trend of the trunk, and remaining relatively short. This fastigiate habit is found in unusual varieties of certain other poplars, other broadleaved trees and a few conifers too. None of these other trees is so easily raised as the Lombardy poplar, for any branch of it can be used as a cutting which easily takes root and starts a new tree; nor are any of them so hardy and free-growing. Lombardy poplar is therefore widely grown in all parts of the temperate zones where people want a tall vertical landscape feature or a tree that will not spread. A row of poplars can also be used effectively as a screen to check the wind, to hide an unsightly building or to check the spread of noise or dirt. The very numerous side branches result in an irregular fluted trunk holding many knots (Plate 124); this is quite useless for veneer, so Lombardy poplar is never planted for its timber.

Lombardy poplar is so-called because it first attracted attention in Lombardy, where many of these trees are grown as landscape features or windbreaks in the level Po valley of Northern Italy. It probably arose as a sport from the common Black poplar, and this remarkable variation must have happened more than once for a female strain is known, though it is seldom cultivated. Nearly all our Lombardy poplars are males, propagated by the infinite division of branches from very few original parent-stock trees; this explains why they all look so much alike.

Botanically the Lombardy poplar is *Populus nigra* variety *italica*. Its French name is *peuplier pyramidal*, and the German *Pyramidenpappel*. Its original home is said to be in Afghanistan. Despite its slender form, it does not grow remarkably tall; a tree near Holyport in Berkshire, at 115 feet, holds the record. There is one fifteen feet round at Upper Edgebold in Shropshire.

### Ontario Balsam Poplar

Certain poplars found wild in North America and Asia belong to the Balsam group, so-called because in spring their buds exude a brown sticky substance with a pleasing scent, which has been likened to the balsams once used to dress wounds or heal sores. A few are cultivated as sources of timber. One, the Ontario Balsam or Balm of Gilead poplar, which is botanically *Populus × gileadensis*, though it is often called *P. candicans*, has been planted quite widely for ornament. In origin it is probably a natural hybrid, and it certainly shows great vigour, producing stout tall stems very fast. Nearly all specimens are female. It has shiny brown angular twigs, and its leaves are large and triangular in shape, and of a pleasing

**Ontario Balsam Poplar**
Male catkin on left, ripening female catkin on right

golden-green colour. Our largest recorded tree, ninety-seven feet by seven feet round, is at Syon House in Middlesex.

Unfortunately the Ontario Balsam poplar is very apt to throw up thickets of strong sucker shoots from its roots, especially after an old tree has been cut down. In this way it can ruin a lot of ground until it has, at some cost and difficulty, been completely rooted out. Happily other Balsam poplars, and other decorative golden-leaved kinds, prove less troublesome. The Western Balsam poplar or Black Cottonwood, *P. trichocarpa*, is widely planted, and its leaves and fruits are shown in Plate 121; it comes from British Columbia.

### Hybrid Timber Poplar

People who raise poplar as a timber crop usually plant one of the vigorous hybrids that have been selected for quick growth and resistance to disease. Of the many named kinds, we can only describe here one, *Populus* 'serotina'. 'Serotina' is here used as a cultivar name; it means 'late-leafing', and in fact the leaves of this poplar do appear later than most. They have at first a curious reddish-brown or bronze colour, but are later mid-green. This tree (Plates 118, 119, 120) is generally called the Black Italian poplar, and it possibly arose in Italy. It is a hybrid between European Black poplar, *P. nigra*, and an American Black cottonwood, *P. deltoides*, which was first noted in Europe in 1755. Most of its characters resemble those of the native Black poplar, but its trunk lacks burrs and there are two little glands at the base of the leaf, close to the stalk. The true strain is male, though similar female hybrids exist.

Nurserymen raise hybrid poplars from foundation stocks, guaranteed true to name, which are managed as coppice. Each autumn the foundation rootstock ripens a 'crop' of cuttings; these are cut off in spring and cut into sections about a foot long. They are then 'struck' by being buried for nearly all their length in another nursery bed, and in their first year they form a root system and a shoot. A year later they are taken from the ground, and the shoot that has formed is cut right back all the way to a strong bud at its base. They are then replanted in the nursery, and this time each grows a much stronger and straighter shoot—the start of the future timber stem. Often this grows six feet tall in one summer. Next winter, these big rooted cuttings, which now have large roots as well as shoots, are planted out, sometimes in the woods but more often beside streams or on odd patches of fertile, drained marshland. Each needs ample growing space, so they are planted at least twenty feet apart.

Later on, their lower side branches are pruned away so that no big knots form where they would spoil, for veneer production, the valuable lower part of the stem. The trees grow remarkably fast, sometimes five feet taller each year for many years, and develop big open crowns. They are felled for timber when comparatively young, after about thirty years growth, and can thus prove very profitable.

Because of their quick growth, the hybrid poplars are often planted as street or park trees. They do well in smoky towns, but need ample room. They also make good windbreaks in the low-lying fen country of East Anglia, where light soils are apt to blow. Within the British Isles poplar growing for timber is done mainly in the south and east of England. On the Continent it is well developed in many countries with suitable lowland ground, particularly Germany, Holland, Belgium, France and Northern Italy. The main markets are match veneers and paper pulp.

# THE CONIFERS

THE conifers or Coniferae are a closely-knit group of trees bearing narrow, needle-shaped leaves that contrast with the broader-bladed foliage of the broadleaved trees (discussed on p. 53). They are called conifers, meaning cone-bearers, because most of them produce their seeds in woody cones, though a few have berries; these cones show a wide range of shape and size so they help in identification. Conifers are also called *softwoods*, because the wood of most of them is softer than that of the broadleaved hardwoods, though a few yield hard timbers. Included with them here, though it actually has a class of its own, is the Maidenhair tree (p. 263), which bears peculiar two-lobed broad leaves.

Botanically the conifers and the Maidenhair tree are all Gymnosperms, meaning 'naked seeded', because their tiny ovules, which later become seeds, are never concealed in an ovary but lie exposed on a scale. This is a fine point needing dissection to check, for to the ordinary observer the ovules of conifers appear to be firmly held in a flower, whilst their ripe seeds are sometimes enclosed in a berry, and often held within a tight-shut cone. Conifer seedlings have varied numbers of seed-leaves, from two or three to twenty or so, depending on species; they are neither Dicotyledons (which always have two seed-leaves) nor Monocotyledons (which have only one seed-leaf).

A useful help to their identification is their evergreen habit; the only common deciduous ones are the larches. All are wind-pollinated which means that none have really showy flowers to attract insects, and all have separate male and female flowers. Nearly all have winged seeds which are spread by the wind. Most have a 'juvenile' pattern of foliage found in seedlings and on leading shoots, which differs from the adult pattern found elsewhere.

Other distinctive features are the complete lack of pores from their wood; and the presence of resin in wood, bark, buds and cones of most kinds. The branching habit of most sorts is very regular, often geometrical in character. They rarely yield coppice shoots, and never produce suckers; they are hard to grow from cuttings or to graft, because of the presence of resin, but most can be raised in these ways if expert care is given.

The naming of conifers can be very confusing. Many kinds have been introduced from other continents and European languages therefore lacked words to describe them; also, the layman does not always recognize the differences between them. In English most have been called 'fir', an old name from Norse *furu* which originally applied only to the tree we now call 'Scots pine'. In France most have been called *sapin*, a name now reserved by French foresters for the European Silver fir, or *sapin argenté*. In Germany the word *Tanne* is applied by non-foresters to both the *Rottanne*, our Norway spruce, and the *Weisstanne*, our Silver fir. Luckily foresters in all countries have accepted rules for their common names; these follow, as a rule, the botanical genera; exceptions occur with the names 'cedar' and 'cypress', which are applied to more than one genus.

Most of our conifers belong to one large family, the Pinaceae. To bring out their inter-relationships, the name of each tribe, e.g. Araucarineae, is given also.

The conifers are included in the general keys at the start of this book, but it may help the reader to have, in addition, a further brief key here. It applies only to side shoots and not to leading shoots or to young seedlings, which may have different characters.

15

# KEY TO COMMON CONIFERS

(a) Needles in groups of two, three or five, surrounded at base by papery sheath: Pines (*Pinus*), p. 239.

(b) Needles or leaves in clusters, many together, on knobs or short side shoots.
    (i) Needles evergreen, leathery: Cedars (*Cedrus*), p. 236.
    (ii) Needles deciduous, less tough: Larches (*Larix*), p. 233.
    (iii) Broad leaves, notched at tip: Maidenhair tree (*Ginkgo*), p. 263.

(c) Needles solitary, in two ranks, one on each side of twig, eventually falling singly.
    (i) Needles of various lengths intermixed: Hemlock (*Tsuga*), p. 228.
    (ii) Needles on pegs, which break away if a green needle is pulled, but persist if it falls naturally: Spruces (*Picea*), p. 230.
    (iii) Needles that leave a flat round scar if pulled off, buds blunt: Silver firs (*Abies*), p. 233.
    (iv) As (iii), but buds pointed, brown, papery: Douglas firs (*Pseudotsuga*), p. 225.
    (v) As (iii), but buds enclosed in leafy green scales: Yews (*Taxus*), p. 217.

(d) As (c), but needles fall together with branchlets (often found below tree): Swamp cypress (*Taxodium*), p. 250; redwood (*Sequoia*), p. 247; Dawn cypress (*Metasequoia*), p. 252.

(e) Needles solitary, grouped round the stem, with points pressed against it.
    (i) Foliage flattened, fern-like: Lawson cypress (*Chamaecyparis*), p. 257; Western red cedar (*Thuja*), p. 254; Incense cedar (*Libocedrus*), p. 256.
    (ii) Foliage not flattened or fern-like: Monterey cypress (*Cupressus*), p. 258; Pencil cedar (*Juniperus virginiana*), p. 263 (part foliage only).

(f) Needles solitary, grouped round the stem, points free.
    (i) Needles in groups of three: Juniper and Pencil cedar (*Juniperus*), p. 260.
    (ii) Needles very broad at base: Monkey puzzle (*Araucaria*), p. 221.
    (iii) Needles narrow, points quite free: Japanese cedar (*Cryptomeria*), p. 253.
    (iv) Needles narrow, points close to stem: Wellingtonia (*Sequoiadendron*), p. 249.

# DESCRIPTIONS OF CONIFERS

## Yew

*Taxus baccata*                                          TAXACEAE

Among our native trees the yew stands out by reason of its dark, evergreen foliage, built up of needle-shaped leaves set in two ranks along its twigs (Plate 153). There are many introduced conifers with similar foliage, but the yew differs from nearly all these in having buds with leafy scales; the Californian redwood shows this feature too, but its lower leaves, on each twig, are small, whereas in the yew they are of the same size all the way along. Yew leaves are dark green above, pale green below. When they open the twigs that bear them are green; when they fall, about three years later, the twigs have become brown and bear scaly ridges ending in leaf scars. The leaves are waxy, but never show the white resin bands seen on many conifers; in fact the whole tree is non-resinous. Yew bark is distinctive, being rusty greyish-brown in colour, eventually breaking away in long flakes. The bole is fluted at the base, and large trees look as though they were made up of many stems (Plate 126).

Yews growing in the open develop a typical broad flat

crown (Plate 125), but in the woods this tree can grow tall and slender. The Midhurst yews in Sussex reach ninety-two feet. Yews live longer than any other trees in Europe, growing to enormous girths. Since the heartwood of ancient trees decays, leaving them hollow, no count of annual rings is possible; but estimates based on rate of growth and size make 2,000 years a reasonable figure for exceptional specimens. The stoutest surviving yew in Britain is in Ulcombe churchyard, Kent, and measures thirty-four and a half feet round.

Many reasons have been suggested for the association of yew trees with churchyards. It is probably a mystic, sentimental or religious custom, having nothing to do with the practical provision of bows for archery. Yews doubtless figured in pagan worship, and no doubt the early Christian missionaries preached below evergreen yew trees before their first churches were built. Hywel Dda (Howell the Good), a Welsh king who reigned in the tenth century, set a special value on 'consecrated yews'. Some yews are even older than the ancient churches beside them, suggesting that the church was built on a spot already hallowed by worship. Once the tradition began, it was maintained by deliberate planting, as is still done today.

As a rule the male and the female flowers of yew are borne on separate trees, though exceptions occur. Both sexes open early in the year, from February to March. The male flowers are pretty little groups of yellow stamens, quite obvious to the eye, with anthers set flat across short stalks. The female flowers, rarely noticed, are little greenish structures set in the leaf axils. Although it is classed with the conifers, yew bears a berry, not a cone, and these scarlet fruits, scattered along the dark green leafy branches, form a most attractive sight in midwinter (Plate 153). Each berry has a dull green cup at its base, above which comes the bright spherical coat of sweet pulp, called an aril, which is green at first, ripening later to red. Open at the top, it exposes the olive-green surface of the single hard seed. The pulp is harmless, but has a sickly-sweet taste; the seed is poisonous to humans. Birds swallow it with no ill effects when eating the pulp, and excrete it later, so helping to spread the tree. Soft-billed birds, such as thrushes and migrant fieldfares, seek yew berries greedily in hard weather.

Seed gathered from the tree must be stored in moist sand for fifteen months before it will sprout. It then sends up a shoot with two seed-leaves, followed by needles set singly all round the shoot; normal needles set in two ranks appear in the second year. Early growth is slow, and yews never increase rapidly either in height or girth. There are several ornamental kinds which are propagated by grafting on common yew stock; some have golden foliage (var. *aurea*), others have golden berries (var. *fructo-luteo*). The Irish yew, variety *fastigiata*, was discovered by a farmer named Willis, on the Florence Court estate in County Fermanagh, in 1780; it has an upright form like a Lombardy poplar. Weeping varieties (var. *pendula*) are also grown.

Yew makes an excellent dense evergreen hedge which stands clipping well, but when clipped it never flowers or fruits. It is a good tree for topiary, the peculiar art of training trees into unnatural shapes, from garden seats to peacocks! But yew hedges must never be planted where livestock can reach them because their foliage is, in certain circumstances, poisonous to livestock. Strange to say, sheep, cattle and horses who have constant access to growing yew trees nibble leaves on the lower branches without ill effects, and yew seedlings are eaten along with grass. But the withered foliage, such as is found in hedge-clippings, is highly poisonous, and so are the bark and the seed; they contain the alkaloid taxine.

The yew has a narrow, dead-white sapwood, which contrasts with the rust-brown heartwood below it. This heartwood has remarkable natural durability, and it is said that a post of yew will outlast a post of iron. Rough old yews are still cleft into fence stakes on this account; they also make good firewood. Timber of better quality is nowadays used for artistic furniture, decorative turned work such as bowls, and fine carving; it has a lively grain with very close rings, and can give strong contrasts. In the past its particular use was for the longbow, and though many bow-staves were imported—as they are today—many more were cleft from well-grown native trees. A bow-stave is a section of the trunk, not a branch. Yew is the most elastic of native timbers, as well as a strong one, and its powerful return to its original shape when bent gives impetus to the arrow. But the bow-string must always be loosened when the bow is not in use, otherwise the wood will 'set' in a curve and lose its spring.

Spears of yew wood were used by early prehistoric men during the Ice Ages; one was found in Saxony between the ribs of an elephant! Later, the Vikings used tough yew knot-wood to make nails for ship-building, hence the word 'trenail' for a wooden nail or peg.

Yew grows wild over most of the British Isles. It can be found locally in glens well north in Scotland, though not on outlying islands. It grows high up on chalk downs in the south, but in the north it becomes a lowland tree. An early invader, it reached Britain about 5000 B.C. In the woods it stands more shade than any other tree, and will exist even when overtopped by beech. It casts an even denser shade itself, and no green plant can grow beneath it. It is found right across Europe and Asia, and similar kinds in America give it a spread right round the North Pole. Southwards, yews grow in mountain ranges right to the Himalayas.

*Taxus* is the old Roman name for yew, while *baccata* means 'berry-bearing'. The Greek name, *toxos*, is the root of our word 'toxin' for a poison, and also of 'toxophily', the sport of archery. However, the Latin *taxus* is linked to the verb *texo*, I weave. The bast of yew trees can be woven into ropes or fabric like that of lime (p. 58). For this reason the Norwegians call the yew *barlind* or 'conifer-lime'. Its Danish name is *taks*, from *taxus*.

Alone among our trees, the yew retains its old Welsh name, 'yew' being simply a re-spelling of *yw*, the collective form of *ywen*. The related Gaelic *iubhar* and Irish *iubar* are both pronounced 'ure', and are found in many place names, including Palnure—pool by the yew trees—in Galloway and Inverurie, river-bank of yew trees, in Aberdeenshire. Ewhurst—clump of yew trees—occurring as a village name in Surrey, shows that the word 'yew' was found early in the English tongue, possibly in the days of the Jutes. It supplanted the Saxon name *heben*, which died out in Elizabethan times; this was related to old Danish *iben*, Dutch *iepe*, German *Eibe*, and more distantly to French *if*.

## Monkey Puzzle

*Araucaria araucana*                    PINACEAE: ARAUCARINEAE

'Monkey puzzle' is a name thought up by an English joker who remarked, after pricking his fingers on the foliage: 'It would puzzle a monkey to climb that tree'. It is also called the 'Chile pine' because it grows high in the Andes mountains of South America, while its Latin name is drawn from an Indian tribe, the Araucanos, who gather its large, nutritious seeds as a staple food. Monkey puzzle is easily known by the primitive character of its foliage. The needles are broad at the base, sharp at the tip, dark green, evergreen and leathery; and they persist on the twigs for many years. They are set on the twigs in obvious spirals, and completely hide the buds at the branch tips. When they fade to brown they hang on the twigs for still more years and after they fall their scars still persist, being apparent even on stout main trunks.

The branching is very regular, often quite geometrical in pattern (Plate 127). The bark is grey and fairly smooth, but at the base of the trunk it develops curious folds so that the structure as a whole resembles an elephant's foot. The sap-wood is white and the heartwood pale brown; it resembles the 'whitewood' timber of spruce and is used, in Chile, for joinery and carpentry. Monkey puzzles do not flower until they are well-grown. Some trees produce both male and female flowers;

others produce flowers of one sex only. Fertile seed is rarely produced in Europe. The male flower is a cylindrical green cone about five inches long, built up of oblong scales bearing stamens which shed clouds of golden pollen in October. The female flower is a green globe composed of many narrow scales,

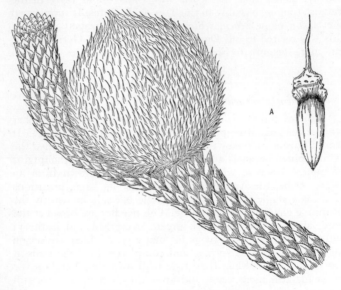

**Monkey Puzzle, with cone**
A, seed, with attached scale and tail

each ending in a slender tail. It takes two years to expand to its full size, about six inches across. After fertilization it needs one or two more years to ripen and turn brown. Below each scale, and firmly attached to it, is a single oblong, pointed seed, over an inch long, which is quite good to eat. Monkey puzzle is easily raised from seed, and when a seed sprouts it keeps its two seed-leaves hidden within the hard brown seed-coat; a carrot-shaped root emerges, from the top of which springs the first upright shoot, bearing typical needles from the outset.

Monkey puzzle was discovered in Chile by a Spaniard, Don Francisco Dendariarena, in 1780, and introduced to England by Archibald Menzies in 1795. We grow it only for ornament, but opinions differ as to its merits! Our tallest tree, of eighty-five feet, is at Bicton, and our stoutest is twelve feet round at Endsleigh, both in Devon. The German name is *Chiletanne* and the French is *araucaria*.

## Silver Firs

*Abies* species                    PINACEAE: ABIETINEAE

We get the name 'silver fir' from the French *sapin argenté*, which arises from two features of the European kind: every needle has silvery white bands of resin to restrict water loss from the stomata, on its under side; and the bark is silvery grey. These needles are ranged in flat planes on side branches, but stand all round the *upright* shoots. The German name of *Weisstanne* has a like origin. In Scandinavia the European kind is *aedelgran*, meaning 'noble spruce'. The word 'fir' is nowadays used by foresters and botanists both in Britain and America for trees of this large distinct *Abies* genus. You can tell them by three features: their buds are blunt and often resinous; each needle when pulled away leaves a neat circular scar, never a peg; the cones are always upright and fall to pieces when the seeds ripen, leaving a central stalk on the twig.

Silver fir bark is smooth at first and bears resin blisters, but eventually it becomes rough and fissured (Plate 129). The timber is white or pale cream all through, though the heartwood sometimes shows a bluish tinge. It has just the same uses as spruce wood (p. 230) and is often marketed as 'whitewood' too. Silver firs produce big volumes of timber fast, so we grow them, though on a smaller scale, as alternatives to spruce. They have a magnificent pyramidal form, and many kinds are planted for ornament.

Their male flowers are upright clusters of yellow anthers which shed wind-borne pollen in May. The female flowers are upright groups of soft scales, green in colour. In most kinds

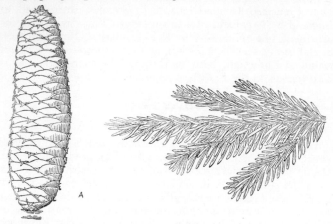

**Silver Fir**
A, cone

they ripen in one season, but the European silver fir takes two years. As soon as the cones are ripe they break up, and their scales, bracts and seeds fall away. Foresters therefore climb the trees in September to pluck the cones before it is too late. Below each scale there are two large seeds, each firmly attached on both sides to a triangular wing (Plate 161, Noble fir). The seeds sprout next spring, but cannot be stored any longer. The seedling has about five seed-leaves which are followed by the same number of primary leaves, placed alternately to them, so forming a rosette; it then forms a winter-bud, and normal foliage follows when the next year's shoot arises.

European silver fir, *Abies alba* (Plates 128, 129), grows wild on the mountain ranges of central Europe, particularly the steep limestone ridges of the Jura where France meets Switzerland. You can tell it from other Silver firs by its buds, which have papery scales *not* encrusted with resin; *alba* means white. This tree was introduced to Britain, and many other European countries, in the sixteenth century. It throve here for 300 years, and a Silver fir near Inveraray in Argyll, 180 feet high and twenty feet round, is probably the largest tree standing in the British Isles. Unfortunately a tiny leaf-sucking insect, the aphid *Adelges nüsslini*, was accidentally brought in from the Caucasus about 1900, and in our mild climate it cripples young European silver firs so badly that they are no longer planted; on the Continent it does little harm.

The giant fir, *Abies grandis*, from the Pacific coast of North America, has been planted on a small scale instead. It has similar needles which are mid-green above, but its buds are resinous, and it is immune to *Adelges nüsslini* attack. It is a fast-growing tree and has reached 164 feet tall, by fifteen feet round, at Ardkinglas in Argyll. *Grandis* means giant.

The Noble fir, *Abies procera* (*procera* also means giant), also comes from Western North America, but tends to be a hardier tree, standing more exposure. This is one of the world's most beautiful conifers; it has upswept needles that are a glistening silver blue on both sides. The cone (Plate 131) has curious reflexed bracts protruding from each scale, and is called a 'feathercone'. Noble fir grows a peculiar trunk, very stout near the foot but tapering sharply higher up. It has reached 150 feet tall, by eleven feet round, at Duncraig Castle in south-west Ross, Scotland. The Latin name of this tree was formerly *Abies nobilis*.

# Douglas Fir

*Pseudotsuga menziesii*          PINACEAE : ABIETINEAE

David Douglas was a bold Scottish botanist who went exploring in the early nineteenth century in North-west

America. In 1827 he sent home the seeds of the magnificent tree (Plate 132) that now bears his name in all countries: it is called *sapin de Douglas* in France; *Douglasie* in Germany; *Douglasden* in Holland; and *Douglasgran* in Scandinavia. The scientific name *Pseudotsuga* was invented by botanists who

**Douglas Fir, with cone**
A, female flower; B, male flower

added the Greek *pseudo*, false, to *tsuga*, the Japanese name for a similar tree (p. 228); *menziesii* records Archibald Menzies, the Scotsman who first discovered the tree in 1791. Until recently it was called *P. taxifolia*.

Douglas fir is easily known by its evergreen foliage. The solitary needles are disposed in flat planes on side branches, but stand all round the *upright* shoots. If you pull one away it leaves a round scar, as a Silver fir needle would do; but the buds are pointed, with papery, dark brown scales, and always lack resin. The male flowers, opening in May, are groups of golden stamens. The female flowers are upright and oval, and consist at first of soft green scales. As they ripen they turn dark brown and come to hang downwards; at the same time a pale brown three-pointed bract develops below every scale. The small winged seeds, two per scale, are shed in autumn. They sprout next spring, and natural regrowth is quite common in Britain as well as in America. The seed is firmly fixed to the wing on one side, but lightly attached on the other; the seedling has about six seed-leaves, followed by normal foliage.

The bark of Douglas fir is smooth at first, and studded with blisters that hold a fragrant resin. Later it becomes remarkably thick, rugged, and deeply fissured (Plate 133). The wood has strongly contrasting bands of pale springwood and dark summerwood, and no matter how fast it grows it always forms a large amount of summerwood each year; it is therefore very strong. The heartwood is somewhat darker than the sapwood, but no more durable. Douglas fir is used, both in Britain and America, for every kind of building, engineering, joinery, fencing and pole construction. It is a major wood of world commerce. Large logs yield plywood which is decorative because of the contrast in colour and texture between the springwood and summerwood.

Douglas fir forms vast and valuable forests down the western seaboard of North America, from Alaska to California. Trees 300 feet tall are still found, and one felled on Vancouver Island in 1895 reached 417 feet tall by fifty-six feet round. In Britain it provides our tallest tree, 181 feet high, at Powis Castle near Welshpool in mid-Wales; another tree at Dunkeld in Perthshire is twenty feet round. Douglas fir is widely planted on fairly fertile soils in glens and lowlands where it grows very fast, often three feet taller each year, yielding good timber in large amounts, but it does not thrive on poor soils or very exposed ground.

# Western Hemlock

*Tsuga heterophylla*                    PINACEAE: ABIETINEAE

The early settlers in New England found a tall tree quite unlike any kind known in Europe. One of them crushed its evergreen foliage and noticed its strong, sour smell; it reminded him of a large poisonous plant that grows beside English rivers. 'Hemlock!' he said, and so these trees gained their remarkable name. The Eastern hemlock of New England has few attractions as a timber tree, but the Western hemlock from Oregon and British Columbia grows so well that it is being planted on an increasing scale in Britain and western Europe. The scientific name *tsuga* was based by botanists on the Japanese name of an Asiatic species. The German name is *Hemlockstanne*, while the French call it *sapin ciguë* meaning hemlock (scented) silver fir.

*Heterophylla* means 'various-leaved' and describes a key feature, for the needles of the common hemlocks are of variable length, long and short ones being intermixed on all the twigs (Plate 135). These needles are short and rather broader than those of most conifers. On side branches they lie in a flat plane, dark green above, paler below. Each arises from a round 'cushion' on the twig. On upright shoots the needles stand all round the twig, and a key feature of hemlock is its drooping leading shoot, designed to shed snow. Altogether the foliage is very pretty, but it is useless for indoor decoration because all the needles fall off a day or two after it is gathered.

The male flowers of hemlock consist of pretty yellow stamens with anthers that are 'peltate', set across the head of the stalk. The female flowers are oval and are made up of green scales. The cones, which ripen in October, are very numerous and conspicuous on the branches. Each is egg-shaped and points

downwards, and every brown, rounded scale holds two tiny
seeds, each bearing a triangular wing firmly fixed on both
sides of it. The seeds sprout readily next spring, and self-
sown seedlings are occasionally seen in the woods. Under
cultivation they need overhead shade for they cannot stand

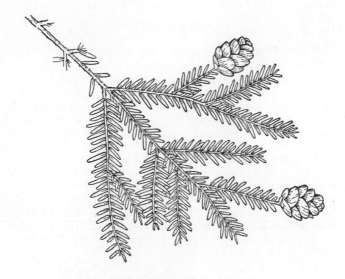

**Western Hemlock**
Twigs with needles of varied lengths, and cones

strong sunshine. The hemlock seedling is peculiar in having
three seed-leaves, followed by the usual foliage.

Western hemlock is widely grown because it stands considerable shade and is suitable for filling gaps, or even planting
below the other trees in open woodland. It rapidly produces
large volumes of a pale brown or yellow timber, with a some-

what darker heartwood. This is easily worked and is very suitable for box-making, joinery, paper pulp and chip-board. Specimen trees hold their lower branches almost to ground level and show a handsome pyramidal form (Plate 134). Our tallest, at Benmore House near Dunoon in Argyll, is 157 feet high, while the stoutest, at Golden Grove in Carmarthenshire, is seventeen feet round.

## Spruces

*Picea* species                     PINACEAE: ABIETINEAE

The spruces are easily distinguished from other conifers by the odd way in which their needles are mounted on the twigs. These needles are evergreen and even in length, and are set singly. Each stands on a little peg projecting from the twig, and if you pull it gently the peg comes away with the needles, together with a short strip of bark. But if the foliage has dried or faded the needle breaks off and leaves the peg behind, and so the older twigs are always studded with little pegs.

No spruce is native to Britain, and the English took this name from the country once called 'spruce', but now known as Prussia. This part of Germany once sent us spruce 'fir' timber from these trees, spruce leather tanned with their bark, and even spruce beer flavoured with their leaves. The Germans, however, call this tree *Fichte* or *Rottanne* (from the reddish-brown of the bark). In Scandinavia the spruce is called *gran*, a word arising from the 'grainy' character of its foliage. The French call it *pesse* or *épicea*, which is linked to Latin *picea*, and also to our word 'pitch' for a black resinous tar originally obtained from spruce trees in Burgundy. The specific name *abies* means silver fir (see p. 223), and is a possible cause of confusion.

Although spruce needles are actually set all round the twigs, on all the side branches they appear to be flattened into a shallow plane with distinct upper and lower sides (Plate 170). Only on upright leading shoots or the drooping branches of certain uncommon kinds, will you see them clearly ranged all round the twigs. In spring the larger branches grow out from whorls of brown papery buds formed the previous autumn, and so distinct annual stages of growth can be seen. But they also bear smaller intermediate leafy shoots which help in identification; these minor shoots leave little knots in the wood, and these too help people to name spruce timber. The bark is smooth at first, breaking away in flat plates later. Open-grown trees have a beautiful pyramidal form. (Plates, 130, 136.)

The male flowers of spruce are little oval groups of golden anthers which shed pollen in May. The female flowers can then be seen as small oval bodies, carried erect on the same twigs; they have soft scales and are violet or purple in colour. They ripen through summer, changing through green to brown cones (Plate 170) which always hang downwards, a useful key feature. In autumn the scales open, and each releases two very small winged seeds. As many as 100,000 may be needed to weigh one pound. The seed sits in a little hollow in the surface of the wing.

When the seedling sprouts next spring it produces a whorl of about twelve needle-shaped seed-leaves, followed by an upright shoot. In its first year it only grows about three inches, so foresters always keep young spruces in the seed beds for two years. They then spend another year or two in a transplant bed. When they are planted in the forest their roots are spread out just below the ground surface or below an overturned turf, for spruce is always a shallow-rooted tree, and roots set deeply would die.

Young spruce trees grow slowly at first, then very fast. They like damp, grassy or rushy ground, and will not thrive among heather. They also like plenty of rain, and are unhappy in dry districts, in smoky places or on chalk. On the western side of Britain they grow very fast and produce huge volumes of timber quickly. Spruce wood is pale yellow in colour; it has a heartwood, but this is just the same shade and has no special durability. Enormous quantities of spruce are imported from northern Europe and North America under the trade names of 'whitewood' or 'white deal', or as paper pulp or manufactured paper. Spruce is the leading joinery and boxwood timber, and is also used in house-building and for ladders. It is moderately strong, easily worked to a good finish, and holds nails and screws well; but little is used out of doors because it does not take preservatives readily. It is the leading raw material for hardboard, chip-board, insulation board, wood wool and paper. Logs with much springwood (p. 3) make the best papers.

The Norway spruce, *Picea abies*, is native to most of northern Europe. It grows up to the Arctic Circle and forms great forests high in the Alps, up to 6,500 feet above sea level. It was introduced to Britain at an early, though unrecorded date and is widely planted everywhere. But though it sets seed freely, self-sown seedlings are rarely seen here; in Norway and Switzerland they spring up like grass! You can tell this spruce by its pleasing mid-green needles, and its long oval brown cones with bluntly pointed scales, each about five inches long and one inch across (Plate 170). Our largest specimen, 142 feet high and fourteen feet round, stands at Inveraray, Argyll.

Nearly all our Christmas trees are Norway spruce; the pleasing custom of using it for winter decoration was brought over from his native Germany by Albert, the Prince Consort, in 1844. Close-grained Norway spruce wood is the only timber ever used for the bellies of violins and similar stringed instruments, and for the sounding boards of pianos, for its resinous nature and the number of rings per inch affect the tone.

Sitka spruce, *P. sitchensis*, takes its name from the small seaport of Sitka, on the Pacific coast of south Alaska; its natural range extends from Oregon to the Arctic Circle. Strains from British Columbia grow remarkably fast in Ireland, Wales and the western regions of Scotland and England. It is now one of our most widely planted trees, but it must have lots of rain, forty-five inches a year or more, to grow well. In America it reaches 200 feet high by thirty-six feet round. Our tallest specimen, 164 feet, is at Murthly in Perthshire; the stoutest, twenty-five feet round, is at Filleigh in Devon.

You can tell Sitka spruce by its blue-green needles—the Americans also call it 'silver spruce'; these needles end in a sharp point, which makes it useless as a Christmas tree. The cone (Plate 137) is very distinctive; it is small, pale brown and every scale has a pretty crinkled edge.

Serbian spruce, *P. omorika*, is very rare as a wild tree. It grows only on a few square miles of limestone near Sarajevo in Yugoslavia, where its local name is *omorika* or *smrc*. Foresters like it because of its very straight stem (Plate 138) and fast rate of growth. The cones are small, purplish-brown, and have rounded scales. There is a specimen ninety feet tall and six feet round at Murthly in Perthshire. The Blue spruce, *P. pungens*, from the deserts of Colorado, is often grown in gardens as an attractive, slow-growing evergreen which bears shiny silvery-blue needles, each ending in a sharp point.

## Larches

*Larix* species                    PINACEAE: ABIETINEAE

The larches are the only common conifers that shed their needles each autumn. Most of these needles are borne on peculiar little knobs or short shoots along the twigs, forming bunches of thirty or so; but the youngest stretch at the tip of every twig has all its needles set singly. When the needles open in April they are bright emerald green and remarkably attractive as an early sign of spring; later they become darker green, and in autumn they fade to a golden shade before they fall. This deciduous habit is linked to the climate where larches grow wild, either in the far north or high up on mountain ranges, where the ground is frozen for most of the year. During the short hot summer, however, they grow very fast. This makes them useful to the forester, but because their crowns of foliage always need full light he cannot grow many trees on one acre, so larch is considered a light timber-yielder.

The male flowers of larch are oval groups of golden anthers which open just as the needles appear (Plate 165), near the tips of the twigs. The female flowers are upright globes of soft scales, either rose-red or white in colour, and because of their pretty shape they are often called 'larch roses'. They ripen rapidly to oval cones that are blunt or even hollow at their tips. Green in summer, the cones become brown by autumn and then hang on the twigs for several years. Only slowly do their scales open to release the seeds; but many fall out when the cones are pecked by birds or nibbled by squirrels. When cones are gathered by the forester he has to use crushing machinery to get all the seeds out. Each little seed has a triangular wing which carries it on the wind; this wing is firmly joined on one side and lightly on the other. The larch seedling bears a whorl of numerous seed-leaves, and then an upright shoot with solitary needles; thereafter all its young shoots have single needles, and all its older shoots bear needles in clusters. Early growth is very fast.

Larch bark is rough, fibrous and deeply furrowed (Plate 140). The timber has a pale yellow sapwood, and a strongly contrasting, reddish-brown, almost terra-cotta-coloured heartwood. It is somewhat stronger than most conifer timbers, and the heartwood is naturally durable. These features make larch very suitable for exacting work, such as bridge-building and ship-building. Venice is built on larch piles, and larch is the only timber used for the outer planking of sturdy fishing drifters still built in Scotland. On British estates larch has long been valued for fencing, gates and building repairs. Much is also used as pit wood. But the tough character of the sturdy timber makes it less well suited for paper pulp and similar wood products. It burns well, but spits out sparks, so it is unwelcome on the home hearth.

Nowadays larches are seldom planted as a major timber crop, but foresters value them for many purposes. They are good 'pioneers' on rough land or old coppice, and a fast-growing first crop of larch can be replaced by some higher-yielding tree later on. They mix well with other trees, and form good early fire-breaks because of their deciduous habit. A well-grown larch is a tree of great beauty, with its main branches sweeping down in great arcs, and its smaller twigs drooping like curtains below; this arrangement gives the leaves good exposure to light, without catching much winter snow.

The European larch, *Larix decidua* (Plate 139), grows on the Alps and a few other high mountain ranges of central Europe, as a timberline bush and also as a fine tall foothill tree. It was introduced, probably from the Italian Tyrol, about the year 1600, and it was planted extensively in Perthshire, mid-Scotland, by the Dukes of Athol from 1738 onwards. It can now be found on nearly every wooded estate in Britain. Strains from the higher mountains grow poorly in Britain, so well-tried 'Scottish' strains are now preferred. You can tell European larch by its straw-yellow twigs, true green leaves and straight cone scales (Plate 165). *Decidua* means leaf-shedding. Our tallest specimen, at Park Hatch, Surrey, reaches 146 feet; our stoutest, at Monzie, Perthshire, eighteen and a half feet round.

Japanese larch, *L. leptolepis*, grows wild on Mount Fuji and neighbouring peaks of Japan. It appears better suited to the British climate and grows faster than the European kind. You may know it by its rust-brown twigs, blue-green needles, and reflexed scales on its cones. *Leptolepis* means thin-scaled. The interesting hybrid larch, *Larix eurolepis*, arose on the Athol estates at Dunkeld in Perthshire in 1904. It grows faster and proves hardier than either parent, and seed orchards have been formed, with European and Japanese larches alternating, to ensure supplies of hybrid seed.

The name 'larch' is based on the original Swiss and German name *Lärche;* the Latin name, *Larix*, has a related origin, though several conifers have been called 'laricio' in southern Europe. The names *lærk* in Danish, *larick* in Scots, and *learag* in Gaelic have a like source. The French call the larch *mélèze*. Tamarack, an American name, cannot be found in Red Indian tongues, and is probably a settler's version of tamarisk, a tree mentioned in the Bible. The Japanese call their larch *kara-matsu*.

# Cedars

*Cedrus* species            PINACEAE: ABIETINEAE

Many trees with fragrant foliage or wood are called 'cedar'. Those of the *Cedrus* genus are evergreen conifers with dark green or bluish-green needles set in bunches of twenty or more on short side shoots which elongate very slowly indeed; this is a key feature, but do not forget that on the leading shoot and the main side shoots, which extend the tree's crown, the needles are set singly. Cedar bark is always grey; smooth at first, it later breaks up into squarish plates (Plate 142). The male flowers do not open until September, and are then seen as upright yellow globes, built up of many stamens, studding the branches. The female flowers are upright, barrel-shaped structures composed of soft green scales. They take two years to ripen into erect brown cones. Each cone is distinctly barrel-shaped, with a flat or hollow top. Its scales are very flat and rounded, and are very slow to open; often they take several years to break up and release the seeds. Below each scale there are two large seeds, each bearing a triangular wing attached to one side of the seed only. Seedlings bear a tuft of numerous seed-leaves, followed by solitary leaves on their first main shoot.

The timber of these cedars is close and even-grained. It has a narrow whitish sapwood and a mid-brown heartwood which is naturally durable. It holds an oil which gives it a delightful fragrance. Being both strong and lasting, it is used for every kind of structural work in the few places where it is abundant, from house-building to railway sleepers. The limited supplies in Europe are used for fine furniture or decorative veneers.

Four species of cedar, all much alike, are grown as decorative trees in western Europe and America. Best-known is the Cedar of Lebanon, *Cedrus libani*, which may be recognized by its level branches (Plate 141). This grows only on the high

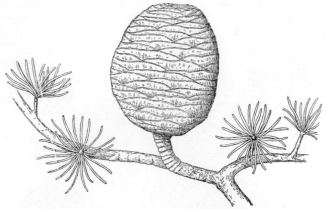

**Cedar of Lebanon, showing old short shoots and cone**

mountains of Lebanon, Turkey and neighbouring lands, where it is a source of wonder to people from the hot, treeless plains. King Solomon bought cedar wood from Hiram, King of Tyre, for the building of his temple, and the trees of Lebanon feature as symbols of joy and prosperity in many verses of the Bible. This tree was introduced to Britain about 1650. It forms handsome specimens with wide-spreading crowns and very stout trunks, suggesting great age. Our tallest tree, at Petworth in Sussex, is 132 feet high, while our stoutest, at Cedar Park in Hertfordshire, is thirty-five feet round. The few small groves carefully preserved on Mount Lebanon include veterans that may be 2,000 years old.

Another species is found on the Troodos Mountains of Cyprus; its scientific name, *C. brevifolia*, refers to the short leaves that aid its identification. On the Indian Himalayas grows the deodar or Indian cedar; its scientific name, *C. deodara*, means 'the gift of god', and it is best known by the drooping habit of its branch tips. In its high, rugged homeland it forms great forests that yield much timber; with us it is grown as a handsome ornamental tree. (See front endpaper, left.)

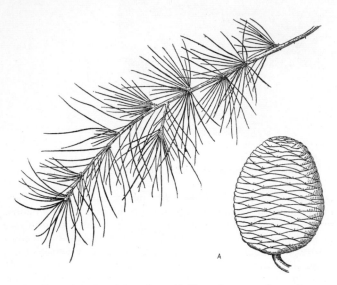

**Deodar, showing long shoot (left) and young short shoots**
A, cone

The Atlas Mountains of North Africa are the home of the Atlas cedar, *C. atlantica*, which has characteristic ascending branches. Its foliage is always bluish-green owing to the resin that restricts water loss under the blazing sub-tropical sun;

the variety *glauca* has exceptionally blue foliage and is often
planted as a striking ornamental evergreen tree.

The Hebrew name for the Cedar of Lebanon was *erez*,
plural *arazim*. The translators of the Bible rendered this as
*cedrus*, the Roman name for a fragrant juniper; and the
*European* names of *cèdre* in France, *Zeder* in Germany, and
*ceder* in Holland and Scandinavia are all based on this root.

# Scots Pine

*Pinus sylvestris*                    PINACEAE: ABIETINEAE

The Scots pine is known at once by its glistening blue-
green foliage and red upper bark, well-shown in the view of a
native pinewood at Glenmoriston, Inverness-shire, that forms
our frontispiece. Closer at hand, the arrangement of the evergreen needles in twos shows it to be a true pine of the genus
*Pinus*, in which the needles are always grouped in twos, threes
or fives. Both tree and timber are, however, often called by
their older name of 'fir', while the imported timber is generally
called 'redwood' (a name that must not be confused with the
Californian redwoods described on p. 247).

The pollen records show that Scots pine invaded Britain
from Europe about 10,000 B.C., and slowly spread to the far
north. During a phase of warm dry climate it formed vast
pinewoods far higher up the hills than it grows today, and its
stumps can be found preserved in peat bogs, over 2,000 feet
above sea level, at many points in Scotland and northern
England. When cooler, moister conditions followed, the pines
gave way to peat-forming plants which checked the growth of
pine seedlings. As settlements spread many pinewoods were
felled for timber or firewood, or cleared to give pastures and
tilled fields, while moorland fires, lit to improve spring grazing,
destroyed great areas. Nowadays the only thriving pinewoods
of natural origin grow in the Scottish Highlands, particularly
in Strath Spey, Glen Affric and Glen Tanar, beside Loch
Rannoch, and around Beinn Eighe. Odd patches of native

pine scrub survive on peat bogs in many parts of England and
Wales; the pollen records prove their continued existence
since prehistoric times. In Ireland the last known native pine,
which grew on the estate of the Earl of Arran at Crossmolina
beside Loch Conn in County Mayo, survived until 1866.

About the sixteenth century Scottish foresters, notably
those on the estates of the Campbells of Glenorchy in Argyll,
began to raise pines for planting. They exposed the newly
ripened cones to the sun or the mild heat of a fire in spring,
so that the scales opened and the winged seeds fell out. These
were sown in nursery beds, and the resulting seedlings were
lifted when one or two years old and transplanted to another
nursery bed, where a further year's growth caused them to
develop a bushy root system. They were then planted out on the
hillsides, about five feet apart. This is basically the same system
that we use today, both for pines and other conifers. Under
cultivation Scots pine proved a hardy and adaptable tree, and
it is more widely planted than any other conifer, though others
are now used in greater numbers; this is because these other
conifers will, on ground that suits them, produce more timber
in less time than do the pines.

The shoots of Scots pine bear long ridges, each beginning
below a pair of needles. As they get older and thicker the bark
becomes scaly, and after the first grey surface has fallen away,
the characteristic orange-red underbark is exposed. On stout
trunks this becomes reddish-grey and quite thick, and it is
broken into broad irregular plates with dark fissures between
them (Plate 144). Each shoot ends in a rust-red, blunt-pointed
winter bud, and when this opens in spring the shoot within
elongates rapidly and its pairs of blue-green needles expand.
The male flowers are also borne on such new shoots (Plate 143);
they are clusters of anthers which open in May and scatter
clouds of yellow pollen, so freely that it can be seen on the
forest floor.

The female flowers appear right at the tip of a newly opened
shoot, being dark red globes about the size of a wheat grain.

After pollination they turn brownish-green, but they only grow slightly larger the first summer. In their second summer they expand into typical cones. By the autumn the shoot on which they stand has grown on again, so ripe cones are always found one 'step' back from the tip of the shoot. When first ripe they are green and the scales are tightly shut; during the winter they turn brown, and dry weather then causes the scales to open and shed their seeds. Each fertile scale has two seeds below it, and each seed is brown and oval, bearing a triangular papery brown wing to aid wind dispersal (Plate 161). As in all pines, the wing holds the seed within two little prongs. Ripe cones attract squirrels, woodpeckers and crossbills, all equipped with sharp teeth or bills to get the seeds out. Empty cones hang on the tree for a year or two, and then fall. On each scale there is a woody surface, called an 'umbo', which aids identification; on Scots pine it is flat.

The seed sprouts in spring on the forest floor, sending up a thin red stalk, topped by a whorl of numerous seed-leaves. From this springs the first upright shoot with true leaves; on this shoot *only* they are solitary; on all later shoots they grow in pairs. On light, sandy soils with little plant cover, pine seedlings grow freely and many pinewoods are renewed by self-sown seed, especially in the New Forest; in fact pines have naturalized themselves on many heaths in southern England. Scots pine seldom makes an exceptionally large tree. The current records are 120 feet tall at Oakley Park, Ludlow, Shropshire, and twenty-four feet round at Guisachan (meaning 'the little pinewood') near Glen Affric in Inverness-shire. The normal life span is about 150 years, but trees 300 years old have been felled in the Queen's Forest of Ballochbuie, near Balmoral in Aberdeenshire.

Scots pine timber is just the same, botanically, as imported red deal or Baltic redwood; this is one of the major timbers of world trade, with a wide range of uses. It is our main timber for house-building, especially joists, rafters and floorboards, and also for railway sleepers, telegraph poles and pit props.

Much is used for boxes and packing cases, fencing and sheds, chip-board, fibre-boards, hardboard, cardboards and paper. It is not naturally durable but takes creosote and other preservatives well, so sleepers, telegraph poles and fence stakes are usually treated before use. The sapwood is yellow, and the heartwood reddish-brown. All the wood is resinous, and is a source of resin, turpentine, pine oil and Stockholm tar.

We call this tree 'Scots' pine to distinguish it from others. Its natural range extends right across north Europe and northern Asia, from the Atlantic Ocean to the Pacific, and south to the Pyrenees, the Alps and Turkey, so it has many names in different tongues. 'Fir', our oldest English and Scots name, is linked to Danish *fyr* and *skovfyr*, and German *Föhre* and *Kiefer*, as well as to Norse *furu*. The word 'fir' has a remote connection with 'fire' from the use of the branches as kindling; while the old Germanic form *foraha* gave rise to the German word *Forst*, and is the source, despite anything the dictionaries say, of French *forêt* and English 'forest'.

Other European names are Dutch *den*, *groveden*, and *pijnboom*, Swedish *tall*, and Finnish *mänty*. The Gaelic name for a pinewood is *guithsaiche*, pronounced 'gyoosie'; it occurs in many Highland place-names, such as Kingussie—the head of the pinewood—in Inverness-shire. The Gaelic word for a pine tree is *giuthas*, which resembles the Irish *giumais* or *gius*. Although truly native pines are very scarce in Wales, a real old Welsh name, *ffynidwydden*, survives. The Roman name was *pinus*, while *sylvestris* means 'of the woods'. The French distinguish this tree as the *pin sylvestre*, though it is also called *sapin rouge* because of its red bark.

## Other Pines

*Pinus* species                    PINACEAE: ABIETINEAE

Many kinds of pines grow in various countries of the northern hemisphere, and all the hardy ones have been tried out in Britain. A few are widely planted for timber and shelter.

Austrian pine, *Pinus nigra* (Plate 147), is best known by its bud, which tapers suddenly to a sharp point, its straight sage-green needles, its tawny-yellow, one-sided cones, its grey bark and its coarsely branched habit. The last feature makes it a poor timber tree, but it is often grown as a shelter-belt on chalk hills or on the coast.

Corsican pine comes from the Mediterranean island of Corsica. It resembles Austrian pine in most features, but its needles are *twisted* (Plate 154) and its branches are light. It is hardy only in the lowlands of Britain, but in dry sunny districts it thrives well and gives good timber at a faster rate than Scots pine, so it is widely planted (Plates 148, 149). A specimen at Cuffnells in the New Forest is 134 feet tall and nearly twelve feet round. A seed is shown in Plate 161. The botanical name of Corsican Pine is now held to be *Pinus nigra* variety *maritima*; hitherto the varietal name *calabrica* has been widely used.

Lodgepole pine, *P. contorta*, comes from British Columbia and is best known by its dark green needles, its odd bark which is black and broken into squarish patches, and its cones which bear a sharp little prickle on each umbo (Plate 146). Because it thrives on poorer ground than other pines, yet produces good timber fast, it is planted on a large scale in Ireland, Wales, Scotland, and locally in England. It is called 'lodgepole' pine because Indians used its straight stems to build lodges or wigwams. At Bicton, Devon, it has reached 103 feet tall by twelve feet round.

Mountain pine, *P. mugo*, can be told by its short green needles and odd cone-scales, which have umbos of various sizes standing out in different directions on each cone. It is occasionally a small slender tree, but more often a straggling bush, useless for timber (Plate 145). Mountain pine grows high on the Alps and other European ranges, where it is highly valued for stabilizing screes and checking avalanches. The Germans call it *Bergkiefer* and the French *pin de montagne*. In Britain it is merely ornamental.

Maritime pine, *P. pinaster*, can be told by its buds, which are long, stout, and bear reflexed scales, its stout, long, leathery needles, its dull red-black, much fissured bark, and its huge cones. It is native to Portugal and the Mediterranean, where it produces saw timber, boxwood, poles, and pulpwood

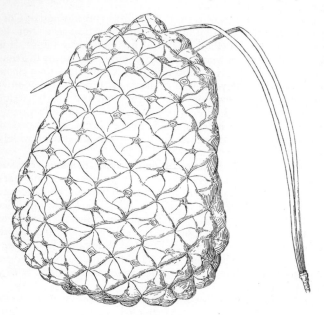

**Stone Pine, cone and paired needles**

quickly. In Britain it has become naturalized around Bourne-mouth (Plate 150). On the Continent, Maritime pines are tapped for resin which flows from shallow cuts made in the sapwood; it yields turpentine and rosin (a yellow waxy solid used mainly to coat printing paper) in substantial amounts. A tree at Foxley Park, Hereford, is 100 feet tall and ten feet round.

Stone pine, *P. pinea*, grows around the Mediterranean, and is sometimes planted in Britain for ornament. It has a broad flat-topped crown, and hence it is called the Umbrella pine too (Plate 151). Its names arise from its huge seeds or stones, called *pignons*, which are used in confectionery as pine kernels. Each has only a vestige of a wing, useless for wind carriage, so the Stone pine relies on chance scattering by animals for the spread of its seed. The cone is large, round and woody, red-brown in colour, and has curious diamond-shaped scales with a hollow around the umbo of each. The bark is red-grey, rough and deeply fissured.

The Bristlecone pine, *P. aristata*, a short rugged tree found in the high alpine deserts of Utah and Nevada, has the distinction of living longer than any other known tree. It grows very slowly, and actual counts of the close annual rings have shown trees only forty feet high and six feet round to be 4,000 years old! It takes its name from little bristles on its cone scales, but you will only see it in botanical gardens.

All the above seven pines have their needles in pairs, as the Scots pine does. Only one pine which bears its needles in *threes* is commonly grown in Britain. This is the Monterey pine, *P. radiata* (Plate 152), which has striking grass-green foliage and thick, deeply fissured bark; its cones are large, woody, one-sided, and persist on the branches for many years. It is found wild on the Monterey peninsula and a few other coastal areas of California, as a low, wind-battered, much-branched tree. In cultivation it grows very fast and straight, yielding large amounts of strong timber, so it is now widely planted in Africa, Australia, New Zealand and southern Europe. In Britain it is considered hardy only in coastal areas; there are a few plantations in Devon and Cornwall, and elsewhere it is seen as a specimen or shelter-belt tree. It shows great resistance to sea winds. Our tallest Monterey pine, 140 feet, at Cuffnells, Lyndhurst, in the New Forest, is higher than any in America; our stoutest, twenty feet round, is at Castle Horneck in Cornwall.

One of Europe's few native five-needled pines is the Cembran pine, *P. cembra*, (Plate 155), which grows on the Alps. Its German names are *Arve* and *Zirbel*, while the French and Italians call it *cembro*. It is a very hardy tree, though slow-growing. Its wood, which is even-grained, pale brown, and easily worked, is used by the Swiss for ornamental carvings, particularly souvenirs for tourists. The cones are large and oval, and the seeds large enough for people to eat—hence the name 'Swiss stone pine'; their wings are very small, and they are scattered by animals. The needles are short, dark green on the lower side and white with resinous wax on the inner one.

An American five-needled pine, sometimes grown in Britain, is the Weymouth pine, *P. strobus*, which has somewhat longer needles and peculiar cones—long and narrow, and curved like a banana (Plate 156). Its pale brown cone scales often secrete blobs of white resin, and its seeds are small and fully winged (Plate 161). The Americans call this tree the White pine, and use its smooth pale brown wood for joinery and pattern-making in engineering; we call it Weymouth pine only because a certain Lord Weymouth planted it widely, in the eighteenth century, on his Longleat estate near Bath. Unfortunately, in both Britain and America it is nowadays severely attacked by a rust fungus, *Cronartium ribicola*, which originally lived only on resistant Asiatic five-needled pines. This fungus must have an alternate host plant—a black currant or some closely related bush. The Americans protect their White pine woods by cutting out the wild currants; but in Britain currants are cultivated so generally that foresters will not form any more Weymouth pine plantations unless and until a rust-resistant strain is found. However, at Puck Pits in the New Forest there is a tree 126 feet tall; and another at Stratfield Saye, Hampshire, girths sixteen and a half feet.

# Californian Redwood

*Sequoia sempervirens*          PINACEAE: TAXODINEAE

To the early settlers on the coast of California, 'redwood' seemed an apt name for this great tree; its very thick, spongy, fissured bark is rust-red in colour, and the trunk holds, within a thin zone of pale yellow sapwood, a stout heart of red-brown timber, very strong and naturally durable. Great forests were soon felled for timber, but others still survive, and the finest redwood groves now form national parks. One splendid tree holds the present world record for height at 365 feet; another, still more famous, has had a roadway cut through its base so that tourists can drive through in their cars. Fallen trees have shown ages exceeding 2,000 years.

The Californian redwood was first noticed by the Spanish explorer Don Gaspar da Pabola in 1769, but fertile seed did not reach England until 1846. It was soon planted as an ornamental tree on many private estates. A magnificent grove now owned by the Royal Forestry Society at Leighton Hall, Welshpool, Montgomeryshire, holds the highest timber volume of any plantation in Britain—16,500 cubic feet (hoppus measure) per acre. Our tallest tree, 135 feet, is at Cuffnells in the New Forest, and the stoutest, twenty-one feet round, is at Taymouth Castle in Perthshire.

The thick bark of the redwood, which helps to shield the trunk from forest fires, makes identification of large trees fairly easy; Californian redwood is readily distinguished from wellingtonia by its very yew-like foliage. On all the side shoots the flat needles stand in two ranks, and as with the yew there is no clear terminal bud, but only a cluster of small scales at each branch tip. The redwood, however, has at the base of each shoot several leaves that are smaller than normal, a feature not seen on yew or other common conifers. On upright shoots the needles are pointed, and are ranged all round the stem.

The male flowers are little groups of yellow anthers borne at

17

the branch tips. Each green female flower stands on its own short stalk, which bears short needles all round it; it ripens in one season to a small oval brown cone made up of open, flat-surfaced scales of irregular outline. There are several seeds below each scale, each being a very small brown grain fringed

**Californian Redwood**
Branchlets bearing smaller leaves towards the base, and a cone

by a thin wing (Plate 161); most prove infertile. The seedling has two flat seed-leaves, and then juvenile foliage made up of solitary needles spaced loosely round the upright shoot; normal foliage appears in the second season. The grown tree has a beautiful open crown (Plate 157).

Note that the 'redwood' timber of British commerce comes

from the Scots pine (p. 239). The name *Sequoia* is based on Sequoyah, an Indian chief; he was the son of a German settler and a Cherokee princess, and he lived in an eastern state remote from California. *Sempervirens* means evergreen. The German name is *Küstensequoie*.

# Wellingtonia

*Sequoiadendron giganteum*    PINACEAE: TAXODINEAE

The American names of 'big tree' and 'giant sequoia' are truly apt for this, the largest of all the trees of the world. It grows wild only in the interior of California, from 4,500 to 6,500 feet above sea level on the Sierra Nevada, where it was discovered by John Bidwell in 1841. Introduced to Britain in 1853, it was at first given the scientific name of *Wellingtonia* in honour of the Duke of Wellington (who had just died), and this word persists in common use. The name *Sequoiadendron* was formed from *Sequoia* (see above) by adding the Greek word *dendron* meaning a tree; *giganteum* means giant. The German name is *Mammutbaum*.

The wellingtonia is often seen in cultivation as a tall park tree of striking pyramidal form. Its foliage consists of short, sharp, grey-green needles that stand close to the twigs, completely concealing them. The male flowers are numerous, but very small, club-shaped clusters of yellow anthers at the twig tips; they scatter pollen in March. The female flowers stand on short stalks, and each is a pale green globe of soft scales bearing tiny spines. They take two years to ripen into egg-shaped brown cones, built up of flat-surfaced scales having an irregular outline and bearing a free point (Plate 159). Below each scale are several tiny brown seeds, edged with a narrow wing (Plate 161). Most of these wind-borne seeds prove infertile. Those that sprout produce four slender seed-leaves, then loosely set, juvenile needles, and next the adult foliage.

The bark of the wellingtonia is quite remarkably thick and spongy; you can strike it without harm to your fist. It is reddish grey in colour and becomes deeply fissured. The trunk beneath it has a pale yellow sapwood and a reddish-brown, strong, naturally durable heartwood; but the tree is too scarce to yield a regular timber of commerce. In California the finest groves are preserved as national monuments. The largest tree,

**Wellingtonia**
Straight, pointed needles clothing the twigs, and a cone

called 'General Sherman', is 272 feet tall, seventy-five feet round, and holds 50,000 cubic feet of timber (by true measure) weighing some 1,300 tons; other American specimens exceed 330 feet in height, and 3,000 years in age. British examples, only 100 years old, cannot approach such dimensions, though there is one 162 feet tall at Endsleigh in Devon, and another one twenty-nine feet round at Crichel in Dorset. A fine group, planted as specimens amid parkland, appear in Plate 158.

## Swamp Cypress

*Taxodium distichum*          PINACEAE: TAXODINEAE

This beautiful conifer (Plate 160) can occasionally be found planted as an ornamental tree beside a lake or river. It is native to the south-eastern states of North America, where it forms large forests in marshy country, and yields a commercial timber. The Americans call it 'baldcypress' because it is one of the few conifers that become 'bald' or leafless in winter; its French name, *cyprès chauve*, has the same meaning, but the Germans call it *Sumpfzypresse*, meaning swamp cypress. It is remarkable in losing its leaves not singly, but by branchlets, for most of its leaves are carried on short side shoots which are designed to break off when the needles fade in autumn. These deciduous needles are rather like those of yew, being flat and set in two ranks; they are pale green in spring, mid-green in summer, and orange-yellow when they fade in autumn. The whole tree then looks like a burning bush and is a truly magnificent sight.

The needles on the upright shoots, and on the permanent side shoots that extend the tree's crown, are different, being set singly all round the twig. The terminal buds are hidden in tufts of leafy scales. When the temporary summer side shoots fall away, a naked bud is seen just above the scar they leave on the permanent shoots; this gives rise to another summer side shoot next year. This tree's deciduous habit may be linked to the fact that it cannot draw water from the soil when the marshes freeze in winter. Even in summer it can only do so by a special device for sending air down into the waterlogged soil. This consists of knee-roots or pneumatophores (literally 'air carriers'), peculiar hollow structures that spring from the roots and project as knobs just above ground level; they are common in America, but are rarely seen in Europe. The bark of Swamp cypress is brown, hard and fibrous. The sapwood is pale yellow and the heartwood reddish-brown; the latter has great natural durability and is used in exacting work exposed to damp, such as window frames and greenhouse construction.

The male flowers of Swamp cypress are borne in showy purplish tassels, about five inches long, near the tips of the branches; each flower has a basal tuft of scales, then about

seven stamens which shed golden pollen in April. The female
flowers are small greenish globes of soft scales, scattered along
the younger twigs. They ripen by autumn to spherical purple
cones, about half an inch across and set on very short stalks.
The scales, few in number, are four-sided and break away as the
cone ripens in November. Each scale releases two little seeds.
The seed is triangular and pointed, with a rough warty coat
and flanges along its edges; it has no true wings but it floats,
and seed dispersal is mainly by water. Each seedling has five
slender seed-leaves, followed by the solitary needles typical of
upright permanent shoots; deciduous branchlets appear later.
In cultivation the Swamp cypress is raised from seed. An
American writer aptly puts it: 'Wet muck forms a good seed
bed'.

*Taxodium* is a botanist's word meaning 'yew-like'; *distichum*, meaning 'ranked in two rows', also refers to the foliage.
Swamp cypress develops a grand rounded crown, rather like
that of a broadleaved tree. It was introduced in 1640. Our
tallest specimen, owned by the Earl of Radnor, grows at
Longford Castle near Salisbury and scales 112 feet; the
stoutest, seventeen feet round, is at Burwood Park in Surrey.

# Dawn Cypress

*Metasequoia glyptostroboides*   PINACEAE : TAXODINEAE

In 1944 a Chinese forester named Tsang Wang went
exploring south of the town of Wan-hsien in Sze-chwan,
south-west China. He crossed a range of limestone hills to a
land-locked valley drained by a river that plunged through
underground caverns on its way to the sea. On its banks he
found the *shui-hsa*, or water fir, a tree hitherto known to
science only in fossil form. Its seeds were sent to America and
Europe, and it is now raised, though mainly from cuttings, as
a curious decorative tree for parks and gardens (Plate 162).
In appearance it is very like the Swamp cypress, and it sheds
its yew-like foliage each autumn in the same way, with whole

branchlets dropping off. But it can easily be recognized, even when leafless, by the position of the next season's summer-shoot bud (p. 52); this is below, or occasionally beside the scar of the side shoot (or the side shoot itself if that has not fallen). On all other trees buds appear *above* side shoots, so this appears to be a primitive feature. The foliage is shown in Plate 174.

Dawn cypress bark is reddish-brown and rough. The sap-wood is buff-coloured and the heartwood orange or purplish; the timber as a whole is quite strong and useful. A tree in the Savill Gardens, Windsor Great Park, is already thirty-seven feet high. The Latin name, an obvious botanical invention, means 'dawn redwood that is like a Canton water pine'.

# Japanese Cedar

*Cryptomeria japonica*          PINACEAE : TAXODINEAE

The Japanese cedar is so-called from its fragrant wood which has a pale yellow sapwood below a grey, hard, fibrous bark, and a dark brown heartwood which is strong and naturally durable. In Japan, where it is called *sugi*, it is a leading timber tree that forms great forests in the hills. We grow it here as an ornamental tree of fine pyramidal form; it has reached 117 feet in height at Woodhouse in Devon, and seventeen feet round at Trevarrick in Cornwall.

You can easily tell Japanese cedar by its needles, which are set all round the twigs but stand clear of them and bend forward, ending in a sharp point; they are evergreen, pale green in colour and conceal the twigs and buds. The male flowers are conspicuous clusters of reddish-brown stamens which shed yellow pollen in April. The female flowers are very pretty, being purplish-green and globular in form, with scales that have recurved points and frilled edges; actually each point is part of a bract fused with the true scale. The cones (Plate 163) are similar in form but brown in colour. Beneath each scale lie two tiny seeds, each edged with a thin wing. The seedling has three flat seed-leaves, and then bears juvenile foliage, which is flatter, softer and more spreading than the stiff-pointed adult leaves that eventually follow.

The Japanese cedar was first encountered by European botanists in Japan in 1692, but was not introduced until 1844,

**Japanese Cedar**
Curved needles, with distinct pointed tips, hide the twigs; the cone has reflexed scales

when seeds were received from China. Though it is considered only partially hardy it thrives in most parts of the British Isles, and has been planted experimentally for timber. The variety *elegans*, which has bronzy-green or even purplish foliage of the loose juvenile type, and forms a shapeless bush, is often planted for landscape effects in gardens. It sometimes sets seed, but is usually raised from cuttings. *Cryptomeria* means 'the hidden part', and was perhaps suggested to botanists by the bract being 'hidden' on the cone scale. The German name is *Sicheltanne*.

## Western Red Cedar

*Thuja plicata*                    PINACEAE : CUPRESSINEAE
The settlers in North America gave the name 'cedar' to a

group of trees with fern-like fragrant foliage. One of these, which comes from the western United States and British Columbia, and has a reddish, fibrous bark, yields an important timber and is widely grown in Europe as a hedge bush, and also as an ornamental and forest tree (Plate 164). It is also called the 'arbor vitae' or 'tree of life'. Its generic name *Thuja* was originally the Greek name for another conifer found in North Africa; *plicata* means 'folded' and refers to the leaf arrangement. In France this tree is called *arbre de vie*, in Germany *Lebensbaum*, and in Scandinavia *kaempethuja*.

The foliage of Western red cedar is *very* like that of Lawson cypress (p. 257); it consists of overlapping needles forming flat 'fronds', and the twigs and buds are completely hidden. But it is tinged with red rather than blue, has an acrid rather than a resinous smell, and is thicker and fleshier at the leaf tips and around the hidden buds. The leading shoot is always erect, not drooping as in Lawson cypress. The male flowers are little oval groups of yellow stamens which shed pollen in May. The female flowers are slender green structures which ripen in October to curious brown cones (Plate 166), quite unlike those of Lawson cypress. Each cone is about half an inch long, and consists of narrow infolded papery scales. The seeds, two per scale, are very small indeed and are almost wholly surrounded by a thin papery wing (Plate 161).

The little seedling of Western red cedar bears only two seed-leaves, then straight needles set in fours all round its young shoots. Only in its second year does it reveal its identity by growing typical flattened foliage. Western red cedar is planted on a small scale in British woods. It is one of the few conifers that thrive on chalk; self-sown trees are fairly frequent. Its foliage is harvested for use by florists, and its poles, which are light, strong and very straight, are used for ladders. Few crops in Europe are big enough, as yet, to yield cedar timber, so big quantities of this are imported from British Columbia. The trunk has a narrow pale yellow sapwood, and heartwood that is at first bright orange-brown, but which weathers on exposure to an attractive silver grey. It is very strong for its weight and naturally durable. In America cedar-wood shingles, which are best cleft and not sawn, have long been widely used instead of roof tiles. Durable Western red cedar is rightly prized for wooden houses, sheds and greenhouses, but in our moist, mild British climate an occasional preservative treatment is most advisable, whatever the makers may say!

## Incense Cedar

*Libocedrus decurrens*          PINACEAE: CUPRESSINEAE

This handsome tree, grown only in ornamental grounds, forms a striking column of evergreen foliage (Plate 167). Its foliage is like that of Western red cedar, but it can be known at once if the fronds of dark green leaves are crushed, for they give forth a strong scent recalling the incense used in certain churches. The word *libocedrus* means 'incense cedar', while *decurrens* refers to the habit of the leaves, which run parallel to the twigs and completely hide them. The male flowers are small oblong groups of yellow stamens. The green female flowers consist of about five oblong scales which ripen to form a brown cone which is cylindrical at first and then opens widely to release about ten little seeds; the cone has a cluster of short, recurved bracts at its base. Incense cedar seeds are peculiar in having a large oval wing on one side and a tiny rudimentary wing on the other. The seedling bears two slender seed-leaves, then juvenile needles standing out from the stalk, and eventually adult foliage.

Incense cedar grows in California, forming a tall tree with pinkish-brown, deeply fissured bark. The fragrant timber has a pale yellow sapwood and a pinkish-brown heartwood. Being naturally durable and easily worked, it is used for fence posts and also for lead pencils. This tree was introduced to Britain in 1853. It has reached a height of 117 feet at Oakley Park and sixteen feet round at Eastnor Castle, both in Herefordshire. The German name is *Flusszeder*, for it grows by rivers.

# Lawson Cypress

*Chamaecyparis lawsoniana*   Pinaceae : Cupressineae

This pleasing tree (Plate 168) is widely grown in gardens
because of the perpetual beauty of it evergreen foliage, which
looks like the fronds of a fern. Each spray consists of many tiny

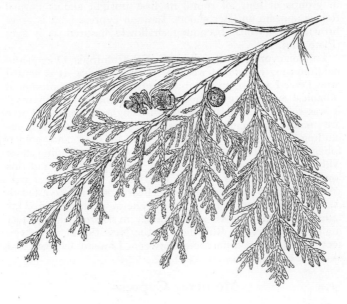

**Lawson Cypress foliage and cones**

blue-green needles closely hugging the hidden twigs and buds;
they are arranged so as to give two flat surfaces to the branch
as a whole. The male flowers appear in April as little club-
shaped, pink-and-brown structures at the branch tips. They
shed golden pollen which is carried by the wind to the female

flowers, small greenish globes on very short stalks. These ripen by autumn to round brown cones, barely a quarter of an inch across, which consist of a few knobbly scales, each with a stalk and a flat top. Below each scale lie two very small seeds, each surrounded by a thin papery wing. The seedling bears two short oblong seed-leaves, then straight needles set in groups of four all round its first upright shoot; normal foliage appears on later shoots. Lawson cypress bark is grey-brown and fibrous, becoming shallowly fissured as it ages (Plate 169).

Lawson cypress grows wild in British Columbia, Oregon and neighbouring regions of western North America. It is named after Peter Lawson, an Edinburgh nurseryman who promoted botanical exploration in those countries. Introduced in 1854, it was soon cultivated in gardens throughout Europe. There are many ornamental varieties, increased by cuttings, including dwarf, bushy, slender, blue foliaged and golden foliaged kinds. The common race has a drooping leading shoot which aids identification. Stems are very apt to fork and this lowers their value as timber. The wood, which has a pale yellow sapwood and a grey-brown heartwood, is harvested in America, however, and used for general construction. Our tallest Lawson cypress, at Endsleigh in Devon, is 116 feet high; our stoutest, at Rhinefield in the New Forest, is thirteen feet round. (For differences between Lawson cypress and Western red cedar, see p. 255.)

## Monterey Cypress

*Cupressus macrocarpa*        PINACEAE: CUPRESSINEAE

The name 'cypress' comes from Greek *kyparissos* and Roman *cupressus*, and was first applied to evergreen conifers found around the Mediterranean Sea. Botanists now use the generic name *Cupressus* for those cypresses that have their needles set *all round* the twigs, hiding both twig and bud. The foliage thus looks rather like that of heath plants, and the purpose of the arrangement is to lessen water loss from the leaves in the hot dry Mediterranean summer. The Italian cypress, *C. sempervirens*, is barely hardy in Britain, but another kind from a similar climate is widely grown as a hedge bush and ornamental tree. This is the Monterey cypress, *C. macrocarpa* (Plate 171), from the exposed Monterey peninsula

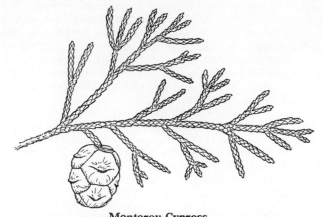

**Monterey Cypress**
The twigs are hidden by adpressed needles; the large cone has broad flat scales, each with a central knob

of California, where a few weather-beaten old veterans brave the Pacific gales.

It has been widely planted in Australia, New Zealand, South and East Africa and other countries of sub-tropical climate, because it produces large quantities of strong, durable wood very fast. In Britain it is only really hardy along the south and west coasts, so it is not planted for timber. Its dark green foliage, quick growth and pyramidal form make it a popular ornamental shrub, and it shows great resistance to sea winds. Our tallest specimen, 117 feet, is at Melbury in Dorset, and our stoutest, twenty-eight feet round, is at Watcombe,

Torquay, in Devon. In inland or eastern districts, hard frosts in severe winters kill off most Monterey cypress bushes.

The male flowers of Monterey cypress are inconspicuous groups of yellow stamens close to the tips of twigs. The female flowers are green globes that ripen to purplish-brown round cones, about half an inch across—the specific name *macrocarpa* means 'large-fruited'. Young trees are raised from seed, and as they are hard to transplant successfully they are often grown in pots. Seedlings have two seed-leaves, then needles grouped in fours, standing out from the first upright shoot, and finally the characteristic heath-like foliage. The bark is greyish-brown and fibrous, and always remains thin. The trunk has a whitish sapwood and a reddish-brown heartwood which is naturally durable.

A hybrid between the Monterey cypress and the Nootka cypress, *Chamaecyparis nootkatensis* from Alaska, was discovered at Leighton Hall, Welshpool, Montgomery, by C. J. Leyland in 1888. It is called the Leyland cypress, × *Cupressocyparis leylandii*. As it is an attractive tree that grows fast and is quite hardy, it is being propagated by cuttings on a growing scale, and it may become a timber-producer.

# Juniper

*Juniperus communis*        PINACEAE: CUPRESSINEAE

The juniper is usually seen as a straggling bush (Plate 172), but some strains develop into slender trees up to fifty feet high and three feet in girth. Its foliage is spiky to the touch and consists of short, sharp needles, bluish-green in colour, covered with a white waxy bloom that restricts their transpiration of moisture. At first sight they look randomly set, but closer inspection shows that they are grouped in threes, which is a key feature (Plate 173). The whole bush has a peculiar fragrance recalling gin, and in fact oil from juniper berries is used to flavour this spirit which would otherwise be odourless and almost flavourless. Oil of juniper is also used in medicine as a flavouring, and as an antiseptic or diuretic; it is distilled from unripe berries.

In spring the juniper bears clusters of male flowers near the tips of its twigs. Each is an oval group of golden anthers which shed abundant, wind-borne pollen. Female flowers, usually on a separate bush, are tiny green structures composed of three seed-bearing scales and take two years to mature. During the first summer the scales swell and the cones become green fleshy globes about a quarter of an inch across; these turn purple as they ripen during the following year, becoming covered with white waxy bloom. They then attract many birds who do not mind their resinous taste, but swallow the fruit and later void the seeds. Within each berry there are from one to three small hard brown seeds; on germination these produce only two seed-leaves, remarkably long and narrow, which are followed by normal foliage. Juniper is rarely cultivated, but can be raised by storing the berries in moist sand for six months, then separating the seed from the pulp before sowing it. Decorative garden varieties, including dwarf and fastigiate forms, are raised from cuttings or grafts on the common stock.

Juniper is hardy and came into Britain very early, about 12,000 B.C., following the retreat of the ice, as early as any tree. On the Continent it grows right to the limits of northern and alpine bush cover. With us, it can now only be found in certain widely scattered districts. On the better soils it was long ago replaced by other trees, while on the poorer ones it has suffered severely from the practice of moor-burning to improve spring grass, since it is very inflammable. In the south of England it survives in Cornwall and is found locally on the chalk downs from Kent to Dorset, tolerating lime-rich soils. In Wales, the Lake District, Galloway and the Pentland Hills it is scarce and local, and only two or three trees remain on the North York Moors. The Scottish Highlands are still its stronghold, particularly the great Forest of Rothiemurchus, now a nature reserve, below the Cairngorms in Strath Spey. In Ireland it is also a local tree. Away to the north it grows in the Outer Hebrides, the Orkneys, the Shetlands and even on Fair Isle.

Juniper bark is fibrous with a pinkish-brown hue. The wood below has a yellowish-white sapwood and a reddish-brown, durable heart; when newly cut it has a pleasant resinous smell. It is so small that it can only be used for small decorative articles. The branches are supple and can be used as bows for archery; in Sweden they were once used for bow-saws as their springiness kept the thin metal blade taut.

The twigs and foliage make good kindling for fires; they also provide the smoke that imparts a delicious taste to juniper-smoked ham.

A dwarf variety, var. *nana* Willd., grows here and there on the Scottish and Irish mountains, and in the northern regions and high mountains of Europe. It is distinguished by incurved, softer, overlapping leaves, low habit of growth and procumbent stem. Both common and dwarf kinds are found right across northern Asia and North America; in fact, right round the North Pole, having the widest spread of any known tree.

We get our word juniper from the Roman *juniperus* which originally meant Juno's pear. The French *genevrier* and, by abbreviation, the word 'gin' come from the same Roman source; *communis* means 'common'. The original name was *cedrus* which now means cedar. In Germany this tree is called *Wacholder*, implying supple wood, and also *Kranawitt* and *Machandl*. Curiously, no Anglo-Saxon name has survived. In Scandinavia the juniper is called *brisk* or *en; enr*, an old Norse form, is found in the name Ennerdale in Cumberland, where junipers grow. In Welsh it is *merywen*, the 'dwarf yew tree', a word which, in its plural form *meryw*, is a possible source of Merrow, where juniper still grows on the Surrey downs. The Gaelic name is *eitean* which is linked with the word *teine* for fire, and records its use as kindling. In Ireland it is called *iubhar creige*, yew of the rocks.

In parks and gardens you will often find small trees that have needle-shaped leaves like those of the common juniper, but intermixed with them scale-like leaves, closely pressed against the stem, which look like those of the Monterey cypress (Plate 174). Here the needle-shaped leaves are considered the juvenile form, since they are found on the young seedling; whereas the scale-like leaves are adult and only appear as the trees grow older. The commonest tree of this kind is the Chinese juniper, *Juniperus chinensis*, which has blunt scale-leaves. The Virginian juniper, *J. virginiana*, which has pointed scale-leaves, is of particular interest because its pinkish-brown, fragrant wood is the best material for the wooden casings of lead pencils. It is also called Pencil cedar, or, in America, the Eastern red cedar; it was introduced by John Evelyn, the author of *Sylva*, about 1660. A similar small juniper with mixed foliage is *Juniperus sabina*, called in French the *savin*, and in German, *Sadebaum*, which grows in the Alps.

## Maidenhair Tree

*Ginkgo biloba*                    GINKGOACEAE

This very pretty tree (Plate 175) is ranked by botanists in a primitive order of its own; it is so ancient that it can be found, in fossil form, in the coal measures laid down millions of years ago, before most modern trees had developed. You can tell at once that it is something strange by its fan-shaped leaf-blade, with veins spreading out in an odd way from the base, and a central notch, which is the source of its specific name *biloba*, two-lobed. Most of the leaves are borne in clusters, on short side shoots that elongate only very slowly. Their long stalks give them a clear resemblance to the fronds of the maidenhair fern. They are deciduous and turn yellow before falling in autumn. The tree grows in size by means of long shoots which bear solitary leaves. It has a roughish, pale brown bark, and a fragrant, pale yellow timber which superstitious Chinese use for coffins. Maidenhair trees grow quite fast and there is one ninety feet tall at Linton Park in Kent, and another thirteen feet round in Kew Gardens, Surrey.

18

Maidenhair trees are either male or female, and as they are usually grown alone as ornamental specimens, fruit is rarely seen in Europe. The male flowers are hanging catkins, borne in groups on short shoots, and consisting of many yellow stamens which shed pollen in spring. The female flower also

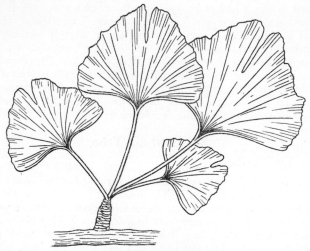

**Maidenhair Tree**
The odd leaves, with diverging veins and a central notch, spring from short shoots

springs from a short shoot; it has a long stalk ending in two tiny green oval ovules, quite naked and unprotected, except for a fleshy rim at their base. Each fertilized ovule ripens to a fleshy seed which resembles a small plum: it has a foul-smelling yellow outer pulp, and a woody stone, which holds an edible kernel, within. The seedling keeps its two seed-leaves in the husk below ground, and its first upright shoot bears rudimentary scale-leaves, followed by normal foliage.

As a wild tree, the maidenhair is very rare, though a few groves are said to occur inland in China. It is widely cultivated in temple gardens both in China and Japan, and it was from such sources that it was brought to Europe about 1727. The name *Ginkgo* is based on a Japanese name; the Chinese call this tree *pa-kwo*. In German it is *Ginkgobaum*, but in French *arbre aux quarante écus*, tree of forty sovereigns, which was the price paid for an early specimen. The maidenhair tree thrives in towns and grows to a pleasing spire-like shape.

# APPENDIX

## Where to See the Trees

THE principal national collections of growing trees are at the Royal Botanic Gardens, Kew, near London, the Royal Botanic Gardens in Edinburgh, and the Dublin Botanic Garden. The Royal Botanic Gardens, Kew, in co-operation with the Forestry Commission, also run the National Pinetum at Bedgebury, near Hawkhurst, Kent; and the Forestry Commission tends the Westonbirt Arboretum, south-west of Tetbury in Gloucestershire. All these places are open, either free or at a small charge, on most days of the year.

The National Trust and the National Trust for Scotland, each own major collections of ornamental trees, open to the public at moderate charges; details will be found in their handbooks. Other collections will be found in public parks and in private gardens occasionally open to the public throughout the country.

## Societies Concerned with Trees

The Royal Forestry Society of England, Wales and Northern Ireland, 49 Russell Square, London W.C.1.

The Royal Scottish Forestry Society, 7 Albyn Place, Edinburgh 2.

The Society of Foresters of Great Britain, c/o Forestry Commission, 25 Savile Row, London, W.1.

The Society of Irish Foresters, Dublin.

Each of these societies publishes a magazine dealing with the growing of trees, both as individuals and timber crops; it also organizes visits to notable forests and arboreta. Details of membership are obtainable from the respective secretaries.

## SELECT BIBLIOGRAPHY

THE principal works consulted in preparing this edition are listed below.

BEAN, W. J., 1951. *Trees and Shrubs Hardy in the British Isles*, Murray, 7th. ed.

BOULTON and JAY, A., 1943, *British Timbers*, Newnes.

DALLIMORE, W. and JACKSON, A. B., 1948, *Handbook of the Coniferae*, Arnold, 3rd. ed.

EDLIN, H. L., 1949, *British Woodland Trees*, Batsford.

EDLIN, H. L., 1953, *The Forester's Handbook*, Thames & Hudson.

EDLIN, H. L., 1956, *Trees, Woods and Man*, Collins, New Naturalist.

EDLIN, H. L., 1958, *England's Forests*, Faber.

EDLIN, H. L., 1958, *The Living Forest*, Thames & Hudson.

EDLIN, H. L., 1962, *Forestry*, Young Farmers Club Booklet, Evans Bros.

EDLIN, H. L. and NIMMO, M., 1956, *Treasury of Trees*, Countrygoer Books, Manchester.

GILBERT-CARTER, H., 1936, *British Trees and Shrubs*, Oxford.

HADFIELD, MILES, 1957, *British Trees*, Dent.

LAIDLAW, W. B. R., 1960, *Guide to Hardwoods*.

SCHWANKL, A., 1956, *Guide to Bark*, Thames & Hudson.

SCHWANKL, A., 1957, *What Wood is That?*, Thames & Hudson.

VEDEL, H. and LANGE, J., 1960, *Trees and Bushes*, Methuen.

# INDEX

This index includes the English, French, German and Latin or 'scientific' names of all the trees described in the text. The third word, or initial, of each scientific name shows the *authority* for it, as explained on page 18. A multiplication sign, ×, indicates a *hybrid*, and single inverted commas a *cultivar*; see pages 19 and 20.